TEACH YOURSELF BOOKS

MECHANICAL ENGINEERING
Volume Two

ENGINEERING COMPONENTS AND MATERIALS

This book gives a general outline of some of the elementary components on which various hand tools have to be used. The components are the various parts which are assembled to form a machine, engine, plant, etc., or parts thereof. It also instructs the beginner in certain every-day principles of construction encountered in Mechanical Engineering practice. S.I. units are incorporated and the text is illustrated throughout.

The author gives some clear and exceptionally well illustrated descriptions of the more common engineering components. There is also an introductory survey of the general engineering materials in use today, and a brief explanation of the test procedure for these. . . . A grand little book which will be of immense value to the student of engineering and the interested layman.

The Technical Journal

TEACH YOURSELF MECHANICAL ENGINEERING

VOLUME TWO

ENGINEERING
COMPONENTS
AND MATERIALS

Written and Illustrated by

A. E. PEATFIELD, A.M.I.Mech.E., A.M.I.Struct.E.

Chartered Mechanical Engineer, Chartered Structural Engineer

TEACH YOURSELF BOOKS

ST. PAUL'S HOUSE WARWICK LANE LONDON EC4

First published 1951
This edition 1971

ISBN 0 340 05651 7

Printed in Great Britain for The English Universities Press, Ltd.,
by Richard Clay (The Chaucer Press), Ltd., Bungay, Suffolk

PREFACE

THE apprentice, or student, having read and studied Volume I (" Hand Tools and Their Uses "), may now give consideration to " Engineering Components, Materials, Testing, Etc."

This book gives a general outline of some of the elementary " components " on which various " hand tools " have to be used. The " components " are the various " parts " which are assembled to form a machine, engine, plant, etc., or parts thereof. It also instructs the beginner in certain everyday principles of construction encountered in Mechanical Engineering practice.

In commencing to study engineering, the student should learn how certain components are used, and their correct application. He should also acquaint himself with the various metals and materials used, together with the specific reason for using them in each case. He should endeavour to distinguish rapidly the different metals by their " appearance ", " grain formation ", and by their " sound " or " resonance " when gently " tapped " with a hammer, and he is advised to " familiarise " himself with various " terms " used in Engineering.

Where special " terms " are used, a brief definition or explanation is given.

In this volume no attempt has been made to deal with detailed engineering design or calculations; the sole object being to introduce to the student the various components and certain engineering practice.

The author wishes to make acknowledgment to the British Standards Institution for their permission to reproduce various tables of screw-threads, pipe flanges, etc.; also to the following firms for supplying data and for granting permission to reproduce illustrations of their products:—

Messrs Cooper Roller Bearings Co., Ltd. (split-roller bearings)
    ,,   Delco–Remy–Hyatt (Hyatt roller-bearings)
    ,,   Ewart Chainbelt Co., Ltd. (industrial chain drives)

Messrs The Hoffmann Manufacturing Co., Ltd. (ball- and
  roller-bearings)
  ,,   Fluidrive Engineering Co., Ltd. (fluid-type
    coupling)
  ,,   Newman Hender & Co., Ltd. (valves, etc.)
  ,,   The Renold & Coventry Chain Co., Ltd. (roller
    chain drives)
  ,,   The Skefko Ball Bearing Co., Ltd. (ball- and roller-
    bearings)
  ,,   Stewart & Lloyds, Ltd. (tubes and fittings)
  ,,   T. Whittle & Sons, Ltd. (link and " vee " belts)
  ,,   Frank Wigglesworth & Co., Ltd. (transmission
    equipment)

                  A. E. P.

PREFACE TO 1970 EDITION

DUE to the change-over of the Engineering industry from
British units to " Metrication ", including S.I. units (International System) together with I.S.O. (International
Organization for Standardization) recommendations, this
book has been completely revised to incorporate the foregoing.

It has been considered advisable, especially for new
apprentices entering the industry, who are conversant with
British units, to insert the latter immediately following the
Metric equivalent, until they become accustomed to working
to Metric units. In certain cases these may not be found
to agree precisely during " conversion " due to a certain
" Rounding-off " being permitted, whilst on the other hand
certain dimensions requiring much accuracy have been
calculated to very fine limits.

Furthermore, especially in the " Machine tool " industry,
many machines are being made to manufacture components
to both British and Metric standards, in order to cope with
the demand for " spares ", which may go on for years, as
it will no doubt take several years for the complete " change-
over " to materialize.

An apprentice draughtsman may be a little apprehensive
when first starting to work to Metric, after having been
perhaps only accustomed to British units; but he will soon
find how easily one becomes used to it after only a short
time, and will eventually find it quite simple, because
everything is in " tens " or multiples of ten.

The beginner should pay special attention to Metric "scales", also the symbols for machining operations, to which he is referred to British Standard No. 308. (Engineering Drawing Practice.)

March, 1969.   A. E. P.

In connection with the revision of this book and combined with its conversion to the Metric System, certain new terms and symbols are referred to. In order to acquaint the reader with these, the following explanations are given:—

Legend.

B.S.I.—British Standards Institution (the British Authority for the instrumentation of the Metric System for Engineering).

B.S.—British Standards (The standard specification for that particular tool, or component used in Engineering).

S.I. unit.—Système Internationale (International System) is a system established in conjunction with the metric system internationally.

I.S.O.—International Standards Organization. An International body which puts forward recommendations considered suitable for international agreement in connection with the agreements on metrication.

I.S.O./R.—Indicates I.S.O. recommendation, followed by the relative number of the recommendation. These recommendations are usually the basis of a British Standard, or intended to be used pending the issue of a Standard at some later date, when definite agreement has been reached.

A full table of ISO Metric Screw Threads is given on pages 183–5 of Mechanical Engineering Volume I, *Hand Tools.*

NOTE

It is strongly recommended that the reader, in order better to understand some of the "terms" mentioned in Chapters 5, 7, 8, 9 and 12 of this book, also studies a book on "Applied Mechanics" or "Strength of Materials", especially if he has no elementary knowledge of the latter.

CONTENTS

PART I

ENGINEERING COMPONENTS

PART II

MATERIALS AND TESTING

PART I

ENGINEERING COMPONENTS

CHAPTER I

BOLTS AND NUTS, SCREW-THREADS, WASHERS, SET-SCREWS, STUDS, GRUB-SCREWS, ETC.

Bolt (Fig. 1)

ONE of the most common forms of " component " is perhaps the bolt. It is used for fastening together any two or more parts of a machine which may require dismantling quickly in any emergency, such as in repair work. If, however, the parts (especially steel plates) are to be secured together permanently, " rivets " would no doubt be used in preference to bolts.

The body of a bolt is called the " shank ", one end of which has a " head ", whilst the opposite end is " *screw-threaded* " to accommodate a " nut " (see Fig. 1*a*). A bolt is often fitted with a plain round " washer ", which forms a sort of " cushion " between the underside of the nut and the face of the workpiece which it secures.

Bolts for general use are usually made of mild steel, but for special work they may be made of high-quality steel, brass, copper, or gun-metal. The shank is screw-threaded for a length slightly in excess of the height of the nut and washer. It is unnecessary and inadvisable to " thread " the bolt lower down the " shank ", for its strength (in shear) depends on its cross-sectional area, together with the quality of steel or material of which it is made. It will be appreciated that the cross-sectional area at the base of the threads is less than that of the plain shank ; therefore if the latter is threaded lower down than necessary its strength is diminished.

In some cases, in addition to an ordinary nut being fitted to a bolt, another nut is fitted, to provide extra security. The latter is called a " lock-nut ", and is usually half the height of an ordinary nut. Whenever a lock-nut is fitted, the bolt must be slightly longer, and its shank must be screw-threaded correspondingly to accommodate both the nut and lock-nut—and a " washer ", if one is to be used. A lock-nut and nut are " locked " together, causing extra pressure to be exerted and thereby assisting in preventing the nut from inadvertently becoming unscrewed, due to vibration, etc.

Several kinds of screw-threads are used, the particular kind depending on the use for which the bolt is intended.

Note.—Screw-threads are fully dealt with later in this chapter, together with other means of preventing bolt-nuts from working loose.

There are many forms of " heads ", each of which is designed for a specific purpose. The most common type is the " hexagon ", as shown in the illustration (Fig. 1a). Incidentally, most types of spanners are made to fit the standard " hexagon-head " bolt.

Some bolts are made of brass—especially those used with electrical apparatus—because brass does not " rust " or " corrode ", like iron and steel, and also because of its better " electrical conductivity ".

Steel bolts are sometimes " galvanised " or " plated " with some other metal, such as cadmium, as a prevention against corrosion. (" Galvanising " is the term given to a process by means of which a coat of " zinc " is applied to an article.)

Square-headed Bolt (Fig. 1b)

This bolt is sometimes used " recessed " into square holes. It is thus prevented by the walls of the recess from turning during the process of having its nut screwed on. In addition, the bolt-head can be flush with the surface of the work to which it is secured.

Cup-headed Bolt (Fig. 1c)

Owing to its " rounded " or " dome-like " shape, this type of bolt-head cannot be held easily while its nut is screwed on to the shank. Either a slot must be made across the " cup ", in order to accommodate a screw-driver blade, or a square neck formed immediately below the head, as shown in Fig. 1c.

Cup-headed bolts with square necks (commonly called " coach-bolts ") are used where one of the parts to be secured together is timber. A square hole is made in the timber, and the bolt-neck is driven tightly into it. These bolts are used considerably for agricultural machinery, which is often constructed partly of timber; and the round head formation of the bolt gives a neat appearance.

Countersunk Head Bolt (Fig. 1d)

This is used when it is desirable to sink the bolt-head to the surface of the work-piece. Such bolts either have a " saw-cut " slot across their heads to suit a screw-driver blade,

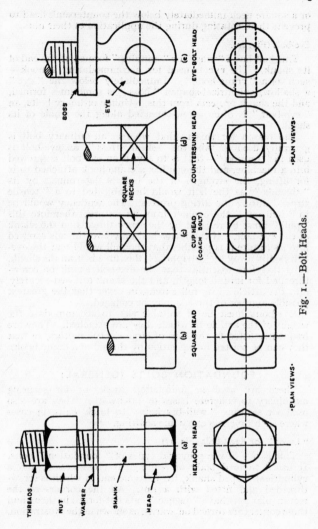

Fig. 1.—Bolt Heads.

or a square neck immediately below the countersunk head to prevent them rotating during the application of their nuts.

Eye-bolt (Fig. 1e).

This bolt has a " ring " or " annulus " formed at the end of its shank. The eye is used for accommodating a hook—such as a " crane-hook ". Immediately below the " eye " a shallow, cylindrical-shaped " boss " is sometimes formed, and the shank projects from this. Unlike ordinary bolts, an " eye-bolt " is often screw-threaded along the whole of its shank.

The reason for this is that whereas an ordinary bolt is generally used to take the " shear stress ", an eye-bolt is used in " tension "—that is to say, if an eye-bolt is screwed into a machine, and the eye has a crane-hook attached to it for lifting, the strength of the bolt is determined by its " threads ", as the bolt would be subjected to a " tensile stress " during the lifting process. The tendency would be to " pull out " the eyebolt from its fixture; therefore this " pull " must be resisted by the screw-threads on the shank of the eye-bolt. If the latter had only two threads screwed into its fixture it is possible that the pull would tear the eye-bolt bodily away by " stripping " the threads from the shank. It is therefore essential that the eye-bolt shank be screw-threaded for its full length, and the shank screwed securely into the article to its full extent, in order that the greatest possible number of threads may be engaged.

Eye-bolts must be of suitable size to accommodate the weight of the article to which they are attached. They are frequently fitted to the tops of large electric motors, so that they can be hoisted into position by the aid of a crane-hook.

FOUNDATION BOLTS (GENERAL)

These are used in foundation work, or for securing machinery to concrete bases or brickwork. They are also used for securing " wall-brackets " to brick walls, in cases where such brackets carry line shafting.

" Lewis " (or Rag-) Bolt (Fig. 1f)

This is one of the principal types of " foundation " bolts. It has a tapered body of rectangular cross-section, and a cylindrical-shaped shank, the extreme end of which is screw-threaded and fitted with a nut. All the corners of the rectangular part have " jagged " cuts hot-forged in them, and these corners are turned outwards, as shown in the illustration.

When the base of a machine or engine has to be securely
fastened to a concrete floor, a " rag-bolt " is used, unless the
work is of a very heavy character.   The body of the rag-bolt
is placed in the wet concrete with its shank projecting above
the concrete level in such a manner that it will accommodate
the base of the machine plus the nut.   In all probability a
bolt would be positioned near each corner of the machine's
base.   The bolts should be supported in position in the concrete until the latter has " set " and " hardened ".   The

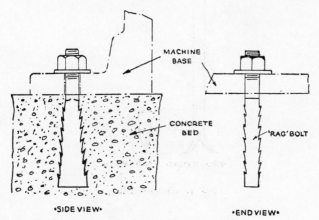

SIDE VIEW   *END VIEW*

Fig. 1*f*.—" Lewis " (or Rag-) Bolt.

machine base can then be placed in position on the concrete
bed, and with the rag-bolt shanks projecting through the base-
plate.   After the machine has been correctly " lined-up "
and levelled it can be fixed in position by the application of
nuts and washers.

" Fish-tail " Bolt (Fig. 1*g*)

This is sometimes used as an alternative to a rag-bolt.
It is of cylindrical cross-section, and one end of it is screw-
threaded and fitted with a nut.   Its opposite end is heated
and, whilst hot, " split " down its centre for a short length,

both ends of the " split " being turned outwards—somewhat resembling a " fish's " tail, from which its name is derived. This type of bolt is cheaper to produce than the rag-bolt, but is possibly not quite so efficient in use. It is quite effective, however, for light classes of foundation work.

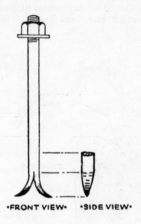

•FRONT VIEW• •SIDE VIEW•

Fig. 1g.—Fish-tail Bolt.

Square-head Foundation Bolt (Fig. 1h)

For heavy foundations, long, plain, straight bolts are used. These have round shanks, and usually either square or hexagonal-shaped heads, and a square shoulder forged immediately next to the heads. On the square shoulder is mounted a mild-steel square washer of stout formation. The concrete is placed all around these bolts and the washer-plates, whilst the screwed shanks are left projecting above the level of the concrete, in order to accommodate the machine base-plate.

In order to provide a stronger fixing for the machine, instead of using a heavy, square washer-plate on each bolt, one long, rectangular plate is sometimes used in conjunction

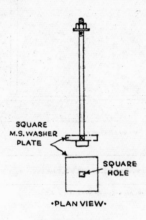

SQUARE
M.S. WASHER
PLATE

SQUARE
HOLE

•PLAN VIEW•

Fig. 1*h*.—Square-head Foundation Bolt.

with two foundation bolts. This is called a foundation washer-plate, and has a square hole near each end, through which the square shoulders of the bolts are fitted (Fig. 1*i*).

A washer-plate of this nature may be 3 feet (914·4 mm.) or more in length, with its bolts spaced correspondingly apart. The concrete is placed over the whole area of the plate, which is consequently completely buried. This type of fixing is often used for securing a " winch " or a fixed crane base in position, as these are subjected to an upward " pull " effect.

Other special types of bolts are, of course, used in engineering, but the scope of this book is to introduce to the beginner types which are most commonly used.

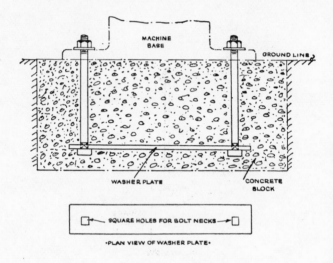

MACHINE BASE

GROUND LINE

WASHER PLATE

CONCRETE BLOCK

SQUARE HOLES FOR BOLT NECKS

·PLAN VIEW OF WASHER PLATE·

Fig. 1*i*.—Two Foundation Bolts Fitted with One Long Washer-plate.

BOLT SCREW-THREADS

Whitworth Type (Figs. 2 and 2*a*)

Many different types of threads are used for the screw-threading of bolts. The commonest form of British thread is the " Whitworth ". In cross-section this is the simplest form of V thread.

The " pitch " of a " single "-type thread is the distance of

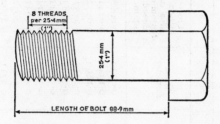

Fig. 2.—Standard " Whitworth " Bolt 25·4 mm. (1 inch)
Diameter, 88·90 mm. (3½ inches) Long.

the centre of one thread from the centre of the adjoining one.
The standard Whitworth thread of a 25·4 mm. (1-inch)-
diameter bolt has a pitch of 3·175000 mm. (one-eighth of an

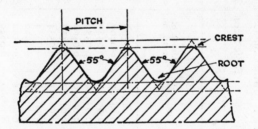

Fig. 2a.—Enlarged Section of Whitworth Bolt Screw-threads.

inch).   Hence, for that size of bolt there are eight threads
per 25·4 mm. (lineal inch) of the screwed shank length.
Fig. 2b gives a table of the British Standard Whitworth
screw-threads for diameters of 3·175000 mm. (one-eighth
of an inch) up to 152·400 mm. (6 inches).
    V threads are used on bolts for general purposes.   The bolts
may be of two classes; those which are used for high-class
work or work of great importance are usually " machined "

Fig. 2b.

Table I. *British Standard Whitworth Screw-threads.*

Basic Sizes. B.S. Whit.

Nominal diameter, in.	Number of threads per inch.	Pitch, in.	Depth of thread, in.	Major diameter, in.	Effective diameter, in.	Minor diameter, in.	Cross-sectional area at bottom of thread, sq. in.
1/8*	40	0·02500	0·0160	0·1250	0·1090	0·0930	0·0068
3/16	24	0·04167	0·0267	0·1875	0·1608	0·1341	0·0141
1/4	20	0·05000	0·0320	0·2500	0·2180	0·1860	0·0272
5/16	18	0·05556	0·0356	0·3125	0·2769	0·2413	0·0457
3/8	16	0·06250	0·0400	0·3750	0·3350	0·2950	0·0683
7/16	14	0·07143	0·0457	0·4375	0·3918	0·3461	0·0941
1/2	12	0·08333	0·0534	0·5000	0·4466	0·3932	0·1214
9/16	12	0·08333	0·0534	0·5625	0·5091	0·4557	0·1631
5/8	11	0·09091	0·0582	0·6250	0·5668	0·5086	0·2032
11/16†	11	0·09091	0·0582	0·6875	0·6293	0·5711	0·2562
3/4	10	0·10000	0·0640	0·7500	0·6860	0·6220	0·3039
7/8	9	0·11111	0·0711	0·8750	0·8039	0·7328	0·4218
1	8	0·12500	0·0800	1·0000	0·9200	0·8400	0·5542

	t.p.i.						
1⅛	7	0·14286	0·0915	1·1250	1·0335	0·9420	0·6969
1¼	7	0·14286	0·0915	1·2500	1·1585	1·0670	0·8942
1½	6	0·16667	0·1067	1·5000	1·3933	1·2866	1·300
1¾	5	0·2000	0·1281	1·7500	1·6219	1·4938	1·753
2	4·5	0·22222	0·1423	2·0000	1·8577	1·7154	2·311
2¼	4	0·25000	0·1601	2·2500	2·0899	1·9298	2·925
2½	4	0·25000	0·1601	2·5000	2·3399	2·1798	3·732
2¾	3·5	0·28571	0·1830	2·7500	2·5670	2·3840	4·464
3	3·5	0·28571	0·1830	3·0000	2·8170	2·6340	5·449
3¼	3·25	0·30769	0·1970	3·2500	3·0530	2·8560	6·406
3½	3·25	0·30769	0·1970	3·5000	3·3030	3·1060	7·577
3¾	3	0·33333	0·2134	3·7500	3·5366	3·3232	8·674
4	3	0·33333	0·2134	4·0000	3·7866	3·5732	10·03
4½	2·875	0·34783	0·2227	4·5000	4·2773	4·0546	12·91
5	2·75	0·36364	0·2328	5·0000	4·7672	4·5344	16·15
5½	2·625	0·38095	0·2439	5·5000	5·2561	5·0122	19·73
6	2·5	0·40000	0·2561	6·0000	5·7439	5·4878	23·63

* Dimensionally the ⅛ inch × 40 t.p.i. thread belongs more proportionately to the B.S. Fine series, but it has for so long been associated with the Whitworth series that it is now included therein.

† To be dispensed with wherever possible.

Extracts from B.S. Number 84—1940, Table I, British Standard Whitworth Screw Threads, are given by permission of the British Standards Institution, 2 Park Street, London, W.1, from whom official copies can be obtained.

Note.—For Metric Screw Threads the reader is referred to Tables 1 and 2 of B.S. 3643 I.S.O. Metric Screw Threads, Part I.

all over their surfaces, and are then known as " Bright " types. Those used for work of less importance are made from material in its rough state, as received from the rolling-mills, and these do not have their outer surfaces machined or polished, but are left " black ", hence they are termed " Black " types. *Bright* bolts are usually " fitted " into accurately drilled holes, and are termed " fitted " bolts, whereas *black* bolts require holes slightly larger than the nominal diameter of the bolt concerned. The hole is known as a "clearance" hole. Naturally, bright bolts and nuts are much more expensive to produce than black types, so they are employed only where the extra expense can be justified.

TYPES OF BOLT NUTS (GENERAL)

In addition to the hexagonal type of nut—illustrated in Fig. 1—square nuts are sometimes used.

Another type of nut is the " Wing-nut ", which is intended for hand use, and does not require a spanner for tightening it.

A further kind is a " Thumb-nut ", which also does not require a spanner, but is intended to be screwed between the thumb and fingers.

Wing-nut (Fig. 2c)

A wing-nut has a cylindrical-shaped body which usually tapers slightly towards the top. The body is screwed internally to suit whichever type of thread is used on the bolt. Projecting from each side of the body is a " wing " or lug, as shown in the illustration. This type of nut is used in cases where a quick release is desired, and in instances where a spanner would not be available. It is quite efficient, especially if it is well tightened up and a spring washer used in conjunction with it. It is, however, used only for light classes of work which do not require special security.

A wing-nut is frequently used for securing inspection covers to machinery. It is also used on electrical apparatus— such as " fuse-boxes ", which may require rapid access for inspection. Wing-nuts are often fitted to domestic appliances, for they can be readily manipulated by the thumb and fingers of a housewife who may not be conversant with the use of spanners. Owing to their special shape, wing-nuts are mostly either " forged " or " cast ". They may be made of cast iron, steel, or brass.

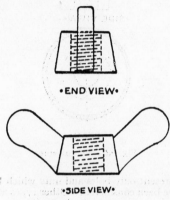

• END VIEW •

• SIDE VIEW •

Fig. 2c.—Wing-nut.

Thumb-nut (Fig. 2d)

This is of shallow, cylindrical shape, with an enlarged top section. It has its edges " milled " or " serrated " in order to give a " grip " when it is used. A thumb-nut, as its name implies, is intended for use by its being held between the thumb and one or more fingers. Its general application is similar to that of a wing-nut, for it does not require a spanner to operate it. Thumb-nuts are used for light classes of work, such as domestic appliances, and they are extensively used on drawing instruments and all classes of fine instruments which require only light pressure. They are neat in appearance and can be easily manipulated.

Small types of thumb-nuts are often silver or nickel-plated for appearance's sake. Larger types are used in mechanical engineering for inspection covers fitted to the valve-gears of engines, etc. Thumb-nuts are mostly made of steel or brass, and are often highly " finished " off by machining and polishing them all over.

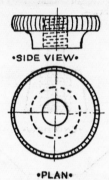

•SIDE VIEW•

•PLAN•

Fig. 2d.—Thumb-nut.

Up to the present only bolts and nuts which have V types of threads have been considered. Other types are often used, however, especially for work of a large diameter.

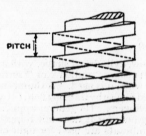

PITCH

Fig. 3.—Typical Square Thread (Single Type).

THREADS

Square Thread (Single Type) (Fig. 3)

For some classes of work " square " threads are used on bolts or spindles. It should be noted that the number of threads per 25·4 mm. (lineal inch) is usually only half that of the V types.

Square threads are mostly used for large-diameter work of a high-class nature, such as on lathes, vices, tension-gear operation on machinery. They are usually formed by machining them in a lathe, whereas V types of threads—especially for bolts—are hand formed by the aid of " stocks and dies " or they are machine-made by mass production methods. " Taps " are used for screw-threading their nuts. These tools are fully described in Volume I.

Fine Screw Thread (Fig. 4)

For small-diameter bolts " fine " threads are used. The term " fine " indicates that the threads are very close to each

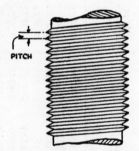

Fig. 4.—Typical Fine Thread.

other, or that their pitch is small. This type of screw-thread is used extensively on light classes of work, such as surveying instruments, small lathes, electrical machinery, etc.

For all fine threads the V formation is used. Bolts having fine threads are usually machined all over, and are therefore of the bright type. An enlarged illustration of a fine thread is shown in Fig. 4.

One of the principal English fine threads is the B.A. type (British Association). A table of British Standard Fine Screw Threads is given in Fig. 4a.

FIG. 4a.

TABLE VIII. *British Standard Fine Screw-threads.*

Basic Sizes. B.S. Fine.

1 Nominal diameter, in.	2 Number of threads per inch.	3 Pitch, in.	4 Depth of thread, in.	5 Major diameter, in.	6 Effective diameter, in.	7 Minor diameter, in.	8 Cross-sectional area at bottom of thread, sq. in.
3/16	32	0·03125	0·0200	0·1875	0·1675	0·1475	0·0171
7/32	28	0·03571	0·0229	0·2188	0·1959	0·1730	0·0235
1/4	26	0·03846	0·0246	0·2500	0·2254	0·2008	0·0317
9/32	26	0·03846	0·0246	0·2812	0·2566	0·2320	0·0423
5/16	22	0·04545	0·0291	0·3125	0·2834	0·2543	0·0508
3/8	20	0·05000	0·0320	0·3750	0·3430	0·3110	0·0760
7/16	18	0·05556	0·0336	0·4375	0·4019	0·3663	0·1054
1/2	16	0·06250	0·0400	0·5000	0·4600	0·4200	0·1385
9/16	16	0·06250	0·0400	0·5625	0·5225	0·4825	0·1828
5/8	14	0·07143	0·0457	0·6250	0·5793	0·5336	0·2236
11/16	14	0·07143	0·0457	0·6875	0·6418	0·5961	0·2791
3/4	12	0·08333	0·0534	0·7500	0·6966	0·6432	0·3249
13/16	12	0·08333	0·0534	0·8125	0·7591	0·7057	0·3911

7/8	11	0·09091	0·0582	0·8750	0·8168	0·7586	0·4520
1	10	0·10000	0·0640	1·0000	0·9360	0·8720	0·5972
1 1/8	9	0·11111	0·0711	1·1250	1·0539	0·9828	0·7586
1 3/16	9	0·11111	0·0711	1·1250	1·1789	1·1078	0·9639
1 1/4	8	0·12500	0·0800	1·3750	1·2950	1·2150	1·159
1 3/8	8	0·12500	0·0800	1·5000	1·4200	1·3400	1·410
1 7/16	8	0·12500	0·0800	1·6250	1·5450	1·4650	1·686
1 1/2	7	0·14286	0·0915	1·7500	1·6585	1·5670	1·928
2	7	0·14286	0·0915	2·0000	1·9085	1·8170	2·593
2 1/4	6	0·16667	0·1067	2·2500	2·1433	2·0566	3·258
2 1/2	6	0·16667	0·1067	2·5000	2·3933	2·2866	4·106
2 3/4	6	0·16667	0·1067	2·7500	2·6433	2·5366	5·054
3	5	0·20000	0·1281	3·0000	2·8719	2·7438	5·913
3 1/4	5	0·20000	0·1281	3·2500	3·1219	2·9938	7·039
3 1/2	4·5	0·22222	0·1423	3·5000	3·3577	3·2154	8·120
3 3/4	4·5	0·22222	0·1423	3·7500	3·6077	3·4654	9·432
4	4·5	0·22222	0·1423	4·0000	3·8577	3·7154	10·84
4 1/4	4	0·25000	0·1601	4·2500	4·0899	3·9298	12·13

Note.—It is recommended that for larger diameters in this series four threads per 25·4 mm. (inch) be used.

Extracts from B.S. Number 84—1940, Table 8, British Standard Fine Screw Threads, are given by permission of the British Standards Institution, 2 Park Street, London, W.1, from whom official copies can be obtained.

Square Thread (Double Type) (Fig. 5)

For large-diameter work " double " or even " triple " square threads are sometimes used. This implies that there may be two or three threads per pitch. Therefore the lineal distance which the nut travels for one revolution is equal to the thread pitch of the screw. This is clearly indicated in Fig. 5.

Left-hand Threaded Bolt (Fig. 5a)

For special cases left-handed bolts are used, on which the thread formation advances in an " anti-clockwise " direction. It is therefore necessary to rotate the bolt-nut in the opposite direction to that of the ordinary right-hand kind in order to tighten it up. The left-hand thread can be applied to square threads as well as to V threads.

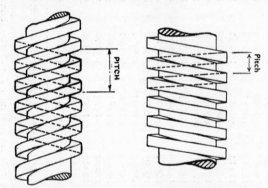

Fig. 5.—Typical Square Thread (Double Type).

Fig. 5a.—Left-hand Thread (Single Type).

FITTING OF BOLTS, NUTS, SCREWS, ETC.

When fixing these in position in machinery it is always advisable to apply a little grease or lubricating oil, especially to the screw-threaded portion. This, in addition to facilitating " tightening " up, by assisting the nut to travel freely along the bolt-threads, also forms some protection against the formation of rust after assembly. It provides for easier unscrewing of the nut when the time arrives for dismantling the machine for any reason. Valuable time can often be saved by this simple precaution.

Bolts are sometimes drilled down the centres of their shanks to reduce their weight. This, of course, somewhat reduces their strength, especially if the bolts are used to resist " shear " stresses, but weight for weight, permits a larger diameter bolt to be used. This practice was at one time used extensively on aircraft and motor-cycle work.

In order to resist " wear and tear ", the outer surfaces of bolts are sometimes " case-hardened ". This means that their shanks, which come under hard wear, would be " heat treated ", in order to form a hard shell or casing on their surfaces. Instances of this application are to be found in the " shackles " or suspension links which carry the laminated springs of motor-cars or railway wagons, which, due to their reciprocating motion, would rapidly wear the bolt-shank surface.

METHODS OF PREVENTING NUTS FROM WORKING LOOSE

Many devices are employed for this purpose, and the main purpose of them is to counteract vibration. However tightly a nut may be " screwed up " originally, sooner or later it may be found to have worked loose. This applies especially to any machine which is subjected to vibration, such as reciprocating screens, concrete mixers, pumps, railway rolling-stock.

Lock-nut System (Fig. 6)

A " lock-nut ", which is usually half the height of an ordinary nut, is used in conjunction with an ordinary nut; the two nuts being " locked " together. The lower nut, after its having been securely tightened on to the bolt, is held firmly by a spanner and the second nut is then screwed tightly on to the lower nut. In theory, the lower nut should be the " thin " one, but as this requires a special thin spanner to retain it whilst securing the top nut, in practice it is more usual to place the ordinary nut below the lock-nut (thin one), which can then be locked by the aid of two normal or ordinary spanners.

A lock-nut is usually made of exactly the same material as an ordinary nut.

Split-pin Method (Fig. 7)

Another practice is to fit a split-pin to the bolt. After the bolt-nut has been finally tightened, a small hole is drilled through the shank-end at a position close to the top face of the nut. The split-pin is then inserted in the hole and its "legs" are opened, as shown in the illustration.

Castle Nut (Fig. 8)

Specially formed nuts are sometimes used in conjunction with split-pins. These have a shallow cylindrical formation at the top of their hexagonal part, and the recesses thus formed will accommodate split-pins. This type of nut is called a "castle" of "castellated" nut, and has a slot on each of its six sides or faces.

Such an arrangement provides three different positions in which the split-pin can be placed, for one drilling of the bolt end. Such a system is very efficient the first time it is used, especially if the bolt-shank is drilled for the split-pin

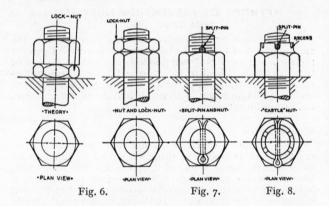

Fig. 6.   Fig. 7.   Fig. 8.

after the nut has been finally tightened. It sometimes happens during repair work, however, that when a dismantled bolt is replaced and tightened up, one of the six slots does not quite coincide with the hole in the bolt-shank. It might also be found impossible to tighten it even a fraction more, in order to bring another slot of the nut to coincide. The mechanic may therefore be tempted to unscrew the nut slightly in order to fit the split-pin. Such practice defeats the whole object of having the nut tightly screwed up, although the latter could not "work off" the bolt while the split-pin is in position.

In such cases it is better to unscrew and remove the nut bodily from the bolt, and file its lower face until it can be screwed tightly into position, with one of its slots coinciding exactly with the hole through the bolt-shank.

Plain Round Washer (Figs. 9 and 9a.)

A plain washer is a flat disc with a hole in its centre through which a bolt, stud, or set-screw can pass. Washers may be made of steel, copper, brass, or fibre, depending on the duty for which they are required. For work of little importance steel washers are made by " punching " them out from " black " steel sheets. During their manufacture they are often slightly " dented ", and the marks of the punch can be distinctly seen on their outer edges, as well as those of the holes.

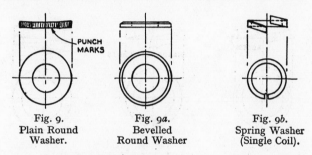

| Fig. 9. | Fig. 9a. | Fig. 9b. |
| Plain Round Washer. | Bevelled Round Washer | Spring Washer (Single Coil). |

For work of importance bright washers which have been machined and polished all over are used. Frequently the top faces of such washers have a bevelled edge, which gives a neater appearance. These washers, being more accurately made, are perfectly flat.

A washer has the effect of assisting in preventing a nut from working loose, to a certain extent by spreading the area of the load. This is particularly so if the nut is screwed extra tightly on to it, so as to compress the washer. The " resilience " or " spring effect " does assist in preventing a nut from loosening, although a plain washer is not considered a normal method for this purpose.

Spring Washer (Figs. 9b and 9e.)

One method of preventing a nut from loosening is to fit what is termed a " spring " washer. There are several forms of these, and each claims its particular merit. A spring washer is a small " helical " spring. When placed in position on a bolt, and the nut screwed on, the " reaction " of the spring, as it is compressed, exerts pressure against the nut and prevents the latter from turning and working loose.

Some of these washers are made with only one " coil " of a split spring, and other types have two coils, as indicated in Figs. 9b and 9e respectively. They are made of a good quality hard " spring "-steel.

Hollow Recessed Spring Washer (Fig. 9c)

A further type of " special " spring washer is one which, in addition to having a " single "-coil helical spring formation,

Fig. 9c.
Recessed Spring Washer.

Fig. 9d.
Hard-pointed Spring Washer.

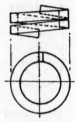

Fig. 9e.
Double Coil Type Spring. Washer.

has its outer edge recessed. It is claimed that the formation of the recess provides an extra spring effect, which thus creates better " reaction " when the nut is applied and subsequently tightened up.

Hard-pointed Spring Washer (Fig. 9d)

Some types of spring washers have hardened points formed at the position of the " split " in the coil. The lower point tends to " dig in " to the underside of the nut. It is therefore claimed that, in addition to the reaction exerted by the spring effect of the washer, the " points " also assist in locating and maintaining the nut in position.

Tab-washer (Figs. 10, 10*a*, and 10*b*)

This is another special form of washer used for securing nuts. Although of similar general shape to that of an

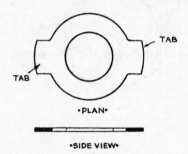

Fig. 10.—" Tab " Washer.

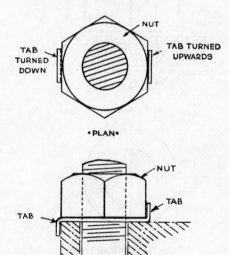

Fig. 10*a*.—Application of " Tab " Washer.

B

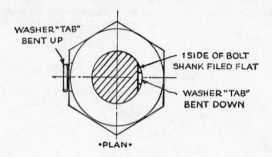

WASHER "TAB" BENT UP

1 SIDE OF BOLT SHANK FILED FLAT

WASHER "TAB" BENT DOWN

·PLAN·

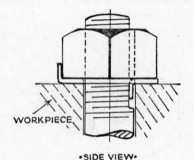

WORKPIECE

·SIDE VIEW·

·PLAN OF WASHER·
PRIOR TO BENDING TABS

Fig. 10b.—Internal " Tab " Washer.

ordinary flat plain washer, it has, in addition, two or more
" tabs " or " lips ", which project from the outer edges, as
shown in Fig. 10. After the nut has been applied and
screwed up tightly over the washer, one of the tabs is bent
upwards and hammered close to one face or side of the nut,
and the other tab is bent downwards and flattened against
the side of the work-piece, as indicated in Fig. 10a. Some
washers have several tabs, so that two or more can be bent
and flattened against the sides of the nut and work-piece
(see Fig. 11).

Tab washers are made of a flexible, soft-quality steel, and
are usually thinner than ordinary plain flat washers. They
can be used only in cases where one edge of the work-piece is

Fig. 11.—Multiple " Tab " Washer.

at a convenient distance from the centre position of the bolt,
in order to allow the tab to be bent over the work (see Fig.
10a).

An alternative type of tab washer is shown in Fig. 10b.
It has one external and one internal tab, and can be used
irrespective of the distance of the bolt from the edge of the
work, but the bolt side must be filed flat in order to accommodate it.

"Locking-plate " (or Stop-plate) (Figs. 12 and 13)

This is another device used for securing a nut in position.
A locking-plate is made from thin sheet steel. After the nut
has been finally tightened, the locking-plate is placed over it
so as to rest flat on the surface of the work-piece. A small

hole is then drilled in the latter, and is tapped or screw-threaded, in order to accommodate a suitable sized set-screw, which secures the locking-plate in position, and consequently secures the nut. An application of this method is shown in Fig. 12.

As an alternative method, a " half-stop " plate can be used, shaped as in Fig. 13.

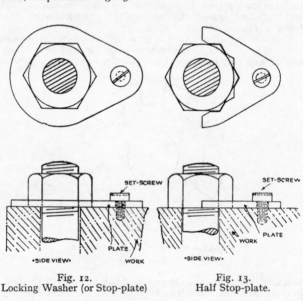

Fig. 12.
Locking Washer (or Stop-plate)

Fig. 13.
Half Stop-plate.

Slotted Nut (Fig. 14)

A nut may be " slotted " horizontally and " sawn " about half-way through. A set-screw hole can then be formed by drilling a hole vertically through the slotted part of the nut. The lower part of the latter can be tapped or screw-threaded to accommodate the set-screw, and the hole in the top part of the nut can be enlarged slightly to form a clearance.

When the set-screw is applied and screwed up tightly, the slot in the nut tends to " close up ". This has the effect of slightly deflecting the internal screw-threads of the nut, causing them to exert pressure on the bolt-shank threads, which assists in preventing the nut from working loose.

Special Compressed Slotted Nut (Fig. 14a)

A further type of slotted nut in general outline somewhat resembles a castle nut, except that the top part is slotted horizontally. After the slots have been cut, the sides of the latter are compressed, partially closing them.

This process deflects the internal threads of the upper-most section, so that when the nut is screwed on to the bolt

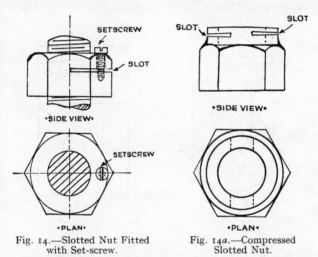

Fig. 14.—Slotted Nut Fitted   Fig. 14a.—Compressed
    with Set-screw.   Slotted Nut.

it has a " binding " effect, through pressure of the nut threads on those of the bolt, for during the application of the nut there is a natural tendency for the slots to open. Constant pressure between the threads retains the nut in position. The effect is greater when it is applied to nuts which have a fine thread.

COMMON METHODS OF PREVENTING NUTS WORKING LOOSE

Of all the various devices used to prevent the loosening of nuts, two of the most commonly used are the spring washer or the split-pin. Either can be fitted with the minimum of effort. A spring washer can often be used in positions which would be difficult of access for a split-pin.

For instance, there may not be room to insert a split-pin and open out its legs with pliers or screw-driver in a bolt placed in a narrow, circular-shaped recess. In such a case a spring washer could more easily be placed over the bolt-shank, and the nut applied and tightened by means of a " tubular " box-spanner.

Furthermore, even if a split-pin could be inserted, and its legs successfully opened, there may not be room to withdraw

Fig. 14b.—Round Taper Washer.

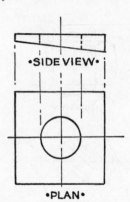

Fig. 14c.—Square Taper Washer.

it later on, when dismantling the machine. Consideration must always be given to the question of dismantling the work, as well as to assembling it.

ROUND TAPER WASHER (Fig. 14b)

Another washer worthy of mention is the " tapered " type. Although this is not used as a method of preventing nuts from rotating or working loose, it can be used to accommodate a nut on a sloping surface of a work-piece.

Mention has only been made so far of nuts and bolts applied to flat surfaces. In certain instances parts of machinery with sloping surfaces may have to be bolted together, in which case round tapered washers may be used.

(Naturally, the taper of the washer must be similar to that of the workpiece to which it is applied.)

These washers are usually " punched " out of tapered steel plate sections, or, for work of a high-class nature, they may be specially machined, in order to give a neat finish. They would then be known as bright tapered washers.

SQUARE TAPER WASHER (Fig. 14c)

These are similar to round tapered washers, but are shaped square. They are used extensively for accommodating nuts

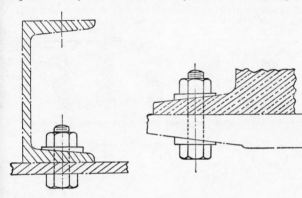

Fig. 14d.—Tapered Washer Used on " Channel " Iron.

Fig. 14e.—Tapered Washer Used on Castings with Tapered Edges.

on the inner faces of rolled-steel sections, such as " joists " and " channels ", so the nuts " bed down " " flush " or flat, otherwise only part of the nut would bear on the surface of the work-piece, which would be unsatisfactory.

For high-class work, bright washers would be used in conjunction with bright bolts and nuts. The " faces " of such washers would be accurately machined, in order to suit both the face of the work-piece and that of the nut. Typical applications of the use of tapered washers are depicted in the illustrations Figs. 14d and 14e, the latter showing the principle applied to the underside of the bolt-head, as well as to the nut.

Machinery subject to vibration, having tapered sections

requiring tapered washers, may need a spring washer. In such a case the latter would be positioned between the top flat face of the tapered washer and the underside of the nut.

In addition, plain round or square-type washers are sometimes used solely as "distance pieces" or "packings". They are often used in this manner where a bolt is too long, or its shank is not screw-threaded sufficiently to accommodate the nut and allow it to be tightened against the work-piece. Such methods are used during the temporary erection of machinery when sufficient bolts of the correct length may not be available.

In an emergency, several washers can be fitted to a bolt which would otherwise be too long for its purpose, and which,

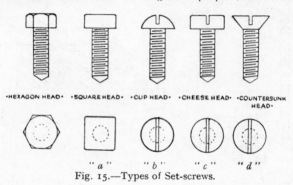

·HEXAGON HEAD·   ·SQUARE HEAD·   ·CUP HEAD·   ·CHEESE HEAD·   ·COUNTERSUNK HEAD·

"a"   "b"   "c"   "d"

Fig. 15.—Types of Set-screws.

if sawn off to a suitable length, would require the screw-threads extended, which is a lengthy procedure.

SET-SCREW (Figs. 15 to 15*d* inclusive)

This component somewhat resembles a bolt, except that it is usually screw-threaded along the entire length of its shank. It is not generally used in conjunction with a nut, but may on occasions be used in conjunction with a lock-nut, in order to secure it in any predetermined position. An example of this is when a set-screw is used for regulating the adjustment of any machine part, and its shank end forms a "stop" (see Fig. 72*a*).

A set-screw is used in conjunction with a screw-threaded hole in the work-piece, whereas a bolt usually fits into plain holes.

In machine construction it is often desirable to attach one part of a machine to another, but it might be undesirable to drill holes through both parts. Furthermore, one of the parts may be much too thick to secure with a bolt. In this

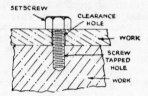

Fig. 16.—Set-screw Used for Securing Together Two Machine Parts.

case the joint can be effected by the application of a set-screw, and the hole screw-tapped to form the threads. The other part of the machine would then be drilled, with a *larger-diameter hole*, through which the set-screw shank could easily

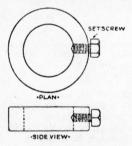

Fig. 17.—Set-screw Applied to a Loose Collar for Securing it to a Shaft.

pass. This is known as a " clearance " hole. A set-screw of suitable length would then be employed to join the two parts, as shown in Fig. 16.

Another application is depicted in Fig. 17, which shows a set-screw applied to a loose collar for a shaft.

Set-screws are also used for securing small brackets to the

face of a " casting ", especially when it is impracticable to drill holes completely through the latter.

Various head formations are used, each depending on the nature of the work. The different types of heads are similar to those of bolts, illustrated in Figs. 15 to 15d.

Where it is necessary to employ set-screws on the internal faces of a machine, especially if on final erection the set-screws will be totally enclosed, some means must be employed to prevent them from working loose. On all set-screws other than the countersunk type a spring washer can be inserted immediately below the head.

If it is essential to use a countersunk set-screw, one well-established method is to make a centre-punch " dent " at the

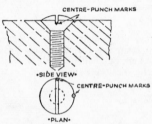

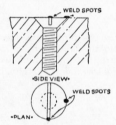

Fig. 17a.—Set-screw Retained in Position by Aid of Centre-punch Mark or " Dent."

Fig. 17b.—Set-screw Retained by " Weld-spot."

junction of the edge of the work and the outer edge of the head. This causes a slight " burr ", and prevents the screw from moving or working loose. When dismantling the machine, these burrs can be lightly " chipped " or filed away, and the set-screw can then be unscrewed. A typical instance of this practice is shown in Fig. 17a.

An alternative method to achieve the same result, and one which has recently rapidly gained favour, is to form a very small " welded spot ", as shown in Fig. 17b. It will be noted that this is formed partly on the edge of the set-screw and partly on the adjacent work-piece, thus uniting the two together. The " spot " can be welded at any point of the set-screw head perimeter, but it is preferable to weld it at one end of the slot, for it can then be easily reached with a chisel point when it is necessary to remove the screw.

" STUD " OR STUD-BOLT (Figs. 18 and 19)

This component, unlike an ordinary bolt, has no head. Instead, both its ends are screw-threaded, one end being screwed into the work-piece, whilst the other carries the nut. A " stud " does not pass completely through the article to which it is attached. It is screwed into the work-piece in a similar manner to a set-screw, and only partly inserted into the work. The shank is not screw-threaded for its entire length, for it is not necessary to " thread " the part that carries the object it is attaching to the machine.

Studs are used extensively for securing cover-plates to machines and cylinder heads to cars. They are most satisfactory because, once fixed, the cover-plate, or cylinder head, can be positioned and retained in position by applying the nuts and washers.

In order to fix a stud into the work-piece a hole must be

Fig. 18.—Round Shank
Type Stud.

Fig. 19.—Square Shank
Type Stud.

drilled and " screw-tapped ". It will be realised that, owing to a stud having no head to which a spanner can be applied, some special means will have to be employed in order to screw it tightly into position. This can be accomplished in several different ways. If the stud is relatively small, pliers or small pipe-wrench may be used by gripping the stud around the unthreaded portion of its shank.

Some studs have square instead of cylindrical cross-sections where the shank is not threaded, as shown in Fig. 19. These can, of course, be screwed into position with a spanner.

If the stud has a plain round shank, and is too large to be successfully screwed into position by gas-pliers or a pipe-wrench, a special " stud-key " would be used. This tool is shown in Fig. 20. It consists of a plain round boss, with a handle. The boss is drilled for a certain distance and is screw-tapped. The top end of the boss is left " blank ", or is not drilled completely through, so it thus forms a " stop " end.

After the stud has been placed in the work-piece and has been screwed in as tightly as possible by hand, the tool is applied and used like a spanner until the stud is fixed tightly in position. In order to withdraw the tool, the plain round shank of the stud must be securely held by gas-pliers or pipe-wrench, otherwise as the stud-key is unscrewed the stud will be withdrawn again from the workpiece, for the adhesion of the key to the stud may be greater than the adhesion of the work-piece to the lower part of the stud shank.

As a precaution against this inadvertent withdrawal, the inner threaded part of the stud-key is often " dusted " over with powdered French chalk, which prevents binding.

As an alternative to the use of a stud-key, a tool known as an " adaptor " can be used. This tool resembles a hexagonal nut, except that it has one " blank " end—or, in other words, it is not drilled and screw-tapped completely through. This

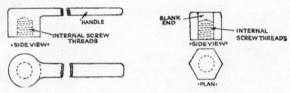

Fig. 20.—Stud-key.   Fig. 21.—Stud-key Adaptor.

tool is used in conjunction with a spanner, in a similar way to screwing a nut on to a bolt. An illustration of a stud-key adaptor is given in Fig. 21.

An independent key, or adaptor, must of course be used for each different diameter stud. Should there be neither key nor adaptor available for a particular stud size, the latter can be successfully fixed in position by the simple use of two ordinary nuts and two spanners. To accomplish this, the procedure is as follows :—

After screwing the stud into the work as far as possible by hand, two nuts are placed on the projecting end. The lower one is firmly held by a spanner, and the *upper nut* is tightened on to it with another spanner. This " locks " the two nuts to each other. The spanner is then removed from the *lower nut*, and, by rotating the top one, the stud can be securely tightened into the work-piece. In order to " unlock " the two nuts, the spanners are again applied to each, and, while firmly holding the top nut, the lower one is unscrewed in the normal manner. The two nuts can then be removed from the stud (see Fig. 22).

In order to safeguard against the inadvertent withdrawal of studs, a little red-lead and oil mixture, or hard-drying

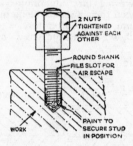

Fig. 22.—Method of Fitting Stud by Aid of Two Nuts in Absence of " Stud-key."

paint, is sometimes applied to the lower end of the stud before it is screwed into the work-piece. The red-lead, or paint, " sets ", and helps in keeping the stud secured (see Fig. 22).

It should be noted that when a large stud is screwed into its hole, some method must be employed to provide for the

Fig. 23.—Improvised Method of Securing a Loose Stud.

escape of air from the base of the hole. This can be effected by making a fine " file-cut " across the threads, as shown in Fig. 22. The edge of a " half-round " file is suitable for the formation of the air slot.

If, after fitting a stud, it is found to be slightly loose, owing to a poor " fit " of the threads (even after it has been screwed well into the base of the hole), it can often be tightened by an

" improvised " method of withdrawing it and making a
" chisel-cut " across the threads. Hard-drying paint can
also be put on the threads; this is most likely to be necessary
when a stud is unintentionally removed when taking off the
nut and cover-plate for inspection purposes (see Fig. 23).

Steel studs screwed into aluminium sometimes " come
away " bodily when their nuts are being unscrewed. This is
because aluminium, being softer than steel, does not bind
quite so effectively on to the stud screw-threads.

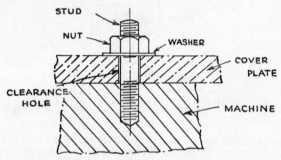

Fig. 23a.—Application of a Stud to Cover-plate of a
Machine.

If it is found that the screw-threads of the work-piece have
broken off (or been " stripped ", as it is called) from the hole,
it must be " re-tapped " to a larger diameter, and a larger
stud fitted. A corresponding clearance hole for that particular stud must be made in the cover-plate. When fitting
nuts to studs, washers are sometimes used, but they are not
always necessary. An example of the application of a stud
when used for securing a cover-plate to a machine is shown in
Fig. 23a.

GRUB-SCREW (Figs. 24, 25, 26, and 27)

This name is frequently applied to all screws of a very small
size. It is mostly used in cases where it is not subjected to
much stress, and is therefore of a light character only. A
" grub-screw " is screw-threaded for its entire length, and has
no separate head (such as a bolt), except in the case of the
countersunk head type, as shown in Fig. 27.

There are several different kinds in use, some of which are shown in the illustrations. That shown in Fig. 24 is the plain " slotted " type. It is screwed " in " or " out " of

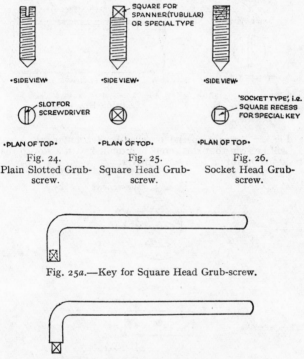

SQUARE FOR
SPANNER (TUBULAR)
OR SPECIAL TYPE

· SIDE VIEW · · SIDE VIEW · · SIDE VIEW ·

SLOT FOR
SCREWDRIVER

'SOCKET TYPE', i.e.
SQUARE RECESS
FOR SPECIAL KEY

· PLAN OF TOP · · PLAN OF TOP · · PLAN OF TOP ·

Fig. 24.
Plain Slotted Grub-
screw.

Fig. 25.
Square Head Grub-
screw.

Fig. 26.
Socket Head Grub-
screw.

Fig. 25a.—Key for Square Head Grub-screw.

Fig. 26a.—Key for Socket Head Grub-screw.

position with a screw-driver. The type illustrated in Fig. 25 has a small square formation at its top end. A special key (illustrated in Fig. 25a) is used for manipulating this screw.

The " socket " kind, with a recess at its top end, is shown in Fig. 26. This screw is manipulated by the key shown in Fig. 26a.

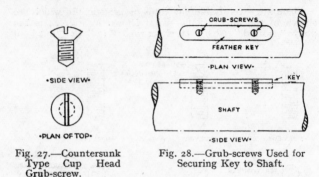

Fig. 27.—Countersunk
Type Cup Head
Grub-screw.

Fig. 28.—Grub-screws Used for
Securing Key to Shaft.

Fig. 27 shows a special bevelled-head countersunk type. It will be seen that this screw is provided with a slot in the head for operation by a screw-driver.

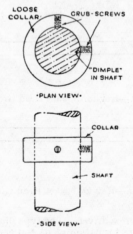

Fig. 29.—Grub-screws Retaining Collar on Shaft.

Grub-screws are usually made of steel, and have the lower end sharply pointed. In some cases the points are

" hardened ". This is done so that the point may penetrate well into the work-piece and ensure a good firm grip. Fine screw-threads are used.

Grub-screws are frequently employed for retaining " feather " keys in the keyways of shafts. An example of such an application is depicted in Fig. 28.

They are also extensively used in " collars " of relatively small diameter, instead of the normal set-screw. For this class of work they are very suitable, and are neat in appearance, for they can be recessed slightly below the surface of the collar, and thus form no dangerous projection. An example of the application of grub-screws to a loose shaft-collar will be seen on referring to Fig. 29.

The bevelled countersunk head grub-screw is often used in such instances, as shown in Fig. 30, for connecting two lengths of handrailing. In this case the screws penetrate through the

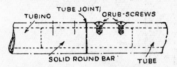

Fig. 30.—Grub-screws Used For Hand-rail Connection.

" wall " of the tubing into a short length of solid bar, which forms the joint for the two lengths of tubing.

For general mechanical engineering work grub-screws are mostly made of steel, but for special cases they may be formed of brass.

In addition to the point of the grub-screw being " case-hardened ", the place where the point penetrates into the work is often very slightly countersunk, in order to fasten the article more securely in position. The slight countersunk recess thus formed is referred to as a " *dimple* ", and an example of this is seen in Fig. 29.

CHAPTER II

SPLIT-PINS, COTTERS AND COTTER-BOLTS

SPLIT-PIN

As the name infers, this is a pin which is split down its centre, thus forming two " legs ". It is made from a " pliable " grade of soft steel, from material of " semi-circular " cross-section bent to form an " eye " from which the legs extend, and when the two legs are closed together, the complete

Fig. 31.—Split-pin.   Fig. 31*a*.—Section of Leg.

shank formation is of circular cross-section (see Figs. 31 and 31*a*).

As previously mentioned in Chapter I, a split-pin is often used for securing a nut in position on a bolt, and to prevent it coming adrift from the bolt-shank. A split-pin is also used in conjunction with a washer for securing a plain round steel pin in position, the end of the latter having a hole drilled through into which the split-pin is fitted. An example of this is shown in the case of the " knuckle-joint " in Fig. 34.

In order to fit a split-pin efficiently after a hole of suitable size has been drilled in the work, the pin is pushed through and the legs are opened or " splayed out " with a screw-driver blade, which is placed between them and gently twisted. This only partially opens the legs. If it is desired to open them more fully, this can be accomplished by pliers, or, if the split-pin is a large one, a blunt chisel and hammer may be used.

The opened legs can either be left in the position shown in

Fig. 32, or they may be bent flat against the bolt-shank, as shown in Fig. 33. The latter position is often more satis-

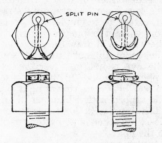

Fig. 32.   Fig. 33.
Methods of Fitting Split-pins.

factory, for, in addition to giving a neater appearance to the work, no objectionable projections are left on which an operator might cut his hand or clothing.

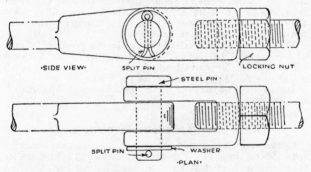

Fig. 34.—Steel Pin Retained in Position by Split-pin.

After prolonged use, split-pins are often found to be troublesome and difficult to extract from machinery to which they are fitted. This is especially so if they have become rusted during use. In such cases it is advisable to inject a little paraffin or " penetrating oil " into the hole around the pin prior to any attempt being made to extract it. This process will tend to dispel or loosen the rust. To withdraw the split-pin, the " bent " legs must be carefully " straightened " and brought close together to resemble as near as possible their original position when the pin was fitted. Then grip the " eye " with pliers and withdraw the pin.

This may be more difficult than it sounds, however, especially if the eye is not in a very accessible place for gripping with pliers. Should this be the case, the " tang "-end of a file can possibly be inserted at right angles to the split-pin, and the file tapped with a hammer in an effort to draw out the pin. This tapping action tends to compress the projecting legs closer together, and better enables them to be pulled through the hole.

Note.—The split-pin's legs, having been bent when they were opened, cannot be expected to return easily to their original straight shape, so they are somewhat " crinkled " at this stage.

Should the legs be badly " twisted ", so that they cannot be brought together in a parallel plane, it may be necessary to cut them off close up to the bolt-shank. If the split-pin is in an accessible place, the cutting can be done with a hack-saw or cold chisel. Should the latter be used, care must be taken not to burr or damage the bolt-threads. After the twisted legs have been cut off, the remainder of the split-pin can be extracted from the eye end.

Should the twisted ends of the legs be in a position difficult of access for a " cutting-off " tool, it may be advisable to cut off the eye of the pin instead. Sometimes, after cutting off one or other of the split-pin's ends, the remaining parts can be " drifted " out of the hole by the use of a small " pin-drift " and hammer.

TAPER COTTER-TYPE SPLIT-PIN (Fig. 35)

Occasionally a tapered round pin of the cotter type may be used for certain jobs. This has its narrow end split down its centre for a short distance, and, after having been inserted into the work-piece, it can be opened out in a similar manner to a split-pin. An illustration of this tapered pin is shown in Fig. 35, and Fig. 36 shows a practical application of its use in conjunction with a washer. This kind of pin is used for larger classes of work, and it is made of mild steel.

For a high-class job the hole for the pin should be tapered similarly to the taper of the pin, but for small diameters and work of less importance a parallel-sided hole will often suffice, although the hole should be of only slightly larger diameter than that of the pin midway along its length. The pin is

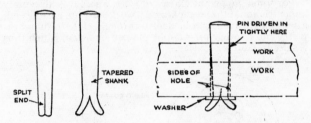

Fig. 35.—Taper Cotter-pin
(with " Split " End).

Fig. 36.—Application to
Work.

hammered into the hole very tightly, then the washer is applied, and the split ends are finally opened. A typical application of this tapered split-pin is shown in Fig. 36.

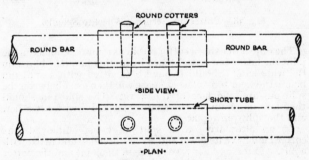

Fig. 37.—Cotter-pin Used for Joint.

COTTER OR COTTER PIN (Figs. 37, 38, 39 and 40)

This is a plain tapered steel pin of either round or rect-angular cross-section. It is used for securely joining to-gether pieces of work where a tight fit is essential. It is therefore the opposite of a knuckle-joint pin, where free movement of the joint is required.

The " cotter-pin " relies entirely on its " driven " fit for retaining itself in position It is therefore essential that it is driven into the hole very tightly, or in due course it may tend to work loose.

For some important classes of work where it is absolutely imperative that the cotter *must not* work loose, its narrow end, after being driven, can be drilled through, close to the work-piece, and another pin or split-pin can be fitted, which thus results in double security.

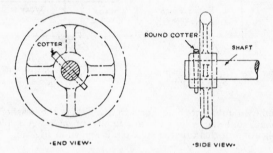

Fig. 38.—Cotter-pin Securing Wheel to Spindle.

The object of using a cotter is that as wear takes place in the joint the latter can be tightened by further hammer-blows on the wide end. Should it have been fitted with a split-pin before the wear took place, a space will then exist between the split-pin and the face of the work. The split-pin should therefore be removed, the space " packed " with a washer, and the split-pin replaced.

As an alternative to a split-pin being employed, the cotter may have its lower end screw-threaded and fitted with a nut. Later, as wear takes place in the joint and the cotter is driven farther into the work, it is then only necessary to adjust the nut position by giving it a few " turns ". In such cases it is usual to fit a washer under the nut. This principle is shown in Fig. 41, but the cotter-bolt shown is of rectangular cross-section.

An elementary use of plain, *round* tapered cotters is shown in Fig. 37. In this case they are employed as a means of connecting together two lengths of round bar, over which a short length of tube is used to form a " sleeve ".

Further examples of the uses of round cotter-pins are demonstrated in Figs. 38 and 39.   In the former the cotter-pin is used to secure the hand-wheel boss to a spindle.   This is accomplished by forming tapered holes through both the

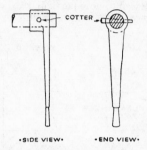

•SIDE VIEW•   •END VIEW•

Fig. 39.—Cotter Securing Lever to Spindle.

boss and the spindle to accommodate the cotter-pin.   Fig. 39 shows a similar application, but in this instance the tapered round cotter-pin secures a small hand lever to a spindle. Both are cheap methods of obtaining fixtures, and should be used only for light classes of work.

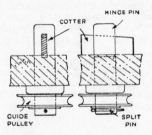

Fig. 40.—Rectangular Cotter Securing Pulley to Hinge-pin.

In addition to cotters of the round type, those of " square " or rectangular tapered section are extensively used.   An application of this rectangular type is shown in Fig. 40. They are used more often when the thin end of the taper is reduced, rounded, and screw-threaded in order to accommodate a nut and a washer. This component is known as a cotter-bolt.

An example of this kind is shown in Fig. 41, in which the centre part of the work-piece is attached to the outer parts. The student is advised to note particularly on which faces of the work-pieces clearances are provided.

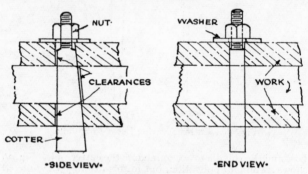

Fig. 41.—Application of Cotter-bolt.

Another everyday example of the use of a tapered cotter-bolt is seen in fixing a bicycle pedal-crank to the axle-spindle. In this case, however, the cotter-bolt is usually of round tapered formation, but along one side it is flattened, in order to fit up to a " flat " surface recessed in the axle-spindle.

A special type of rectangular tapered cotter may also be formed, similar in general shape to that shown in Fig. 40, but its thin end can be split and the ends bent outwards in order to give extra security, or to prevent it from working loose and eventually falling out.

CHAPTER III

KEYS, KEYWAYS, SPLINES ON SHAFTS, ETC. (GENERAL)

In engineering, a " key " is the component used to locate and secure an object in position. The term is usually applicable to the piece of metal which is inserted between a shaft and a wheel in order to retain the latter in a fixed position on the shaft.

The most common form of key is of rectangular cross-section, usually fitted with a head, but sometimes left " plain ". The " body " or shank usually tapers (unless it is of the parallel " sliding " type, which will be considered later on).

One of the most popular types is the " Gib-head ". This is illustrated in Fig. 42, from which it will be seen that the head is of approximately double the depth of the shank. This is because the head is hit with a hammer when driving the key into its position, and because the head can be used by placing a wedge between its inner face and that of the wheel-boss in order to extract the key.

Keys are usually made from good-quality steel, in order to withstand the " shear " stresses which they are called upon to resist. Sometimes " pin-type " keys may be used. These are of circular cross-section, and are chiefly used for work of a light nature.

Keys are made to agreed " standard " dimensions, each depending on the size of shaft diameter for which they are used.

A key, in addition to being a means of securing a wheel to its shaft, also has to take the shear stress developed by the effort to rotate the shaft when the wheel is turned. Hence, if the wheel in question is driven by a belt or chain from any " motive power ", the pull of the " drive " is transmitted to the perimeter of the wheel. At the commencement of this pull, and just while the shaft and wheel are stationary, a " turning moment " is created, which tends to rotate the wheel—and, in due course, the shaft. During this fraction of time (and in so effecting the movement) there is a tendency to

" cut off " or shear the top half of the key. This is what is referred to as the shear stress which the key must be able to withstand or resist. It is because of this shear stress that the key must extend completely through the boss of the wheel in order to obtain the maximum advantage. It will be realised that the instant " power " is applied to the wheel there is an immediate " resistance " or " sluggishness " to the turning effort of the shaft, due to its weight and its contact

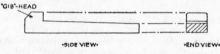

Fig. 42.—" Gib-head " Key.

with the bearings in which it is mounted. Thus it is this resistance which creates the shear stress in the key.

From this explanation it will be realised that it is very essential for the key to be bearing or fitting efficiently into the shaft keyway, and that it should also bear on, or " bed " down evenly on, all the faces of the wheel-boss keyway. Should either fail to do so, the shear stress is transmitted only on to the " parts " which are in close contact, instead of

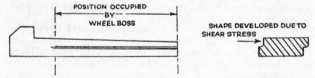

Fig. 42a.—Effect of Loose Fitting " Gib-head " Key.

to the whole area. These parts, therefore, are stressed far higher than they were intended to be, with the result that they will sooner or later fail, and the key may eventually shear off. It is therefore imperative that in all cases keys of suitable size are fitted and that the boss of the wheel is of sufficient depth to withstand the shear force developed.

Unless these precautions are taken, after some use the key will assume a distorted shape, as is shown in Fig. 42a. A similar effect will result if the key is loosely fitted, is too small to withstand the duty it is called upon to perform, or is made of too soft a metal.

GIB-HEAD KEY (Fig. 42)

This is perhaps the best-known type of key used in engineering. It is of rectangular cross-section, the top face of which has a taper of approximately 1 in 64, but its sides are parallel. A " gib-head " key is partly fitted into a recess or key-way of

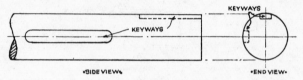

Fig. 43.—Shaft With Key-ways Cut Out Ready to Receive Keys.

the shaft, and partly into the keyway of the wheel-boss which it secures. When any key is fitted *into* a shaft it is known as a " sunk " key.

The boss of the wheel or pulley which the key is used to secure must also be correspondingly tapered in the direction to match the key's taper. When the key is positioned in " work ", and its head is accessible, the latter can also be

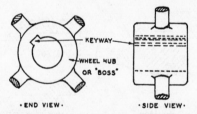

Fig. 44.—Wheel Hub (or Boss) With Key-way.

used in order to extract it. If, however, after assembly of the machinery (the shaft, wheel, bearings, collars, etc.) the key-head is in an inaccessible position, other means would have to be used. Possibly a " key-drift " would be used on the thin end of the tapered key (see Volume I—Figs. 52 and 52*a*). By driving in the key-drift at the opposite end to that of the key's head, the wheel-boss and key are detached.

The key-way which is formed in the shaft is usually of greater length than the key, and the keyway of the wheel extends completely through the boss. By such an arrangement latitude is provided for positioning the wheel-boss, and

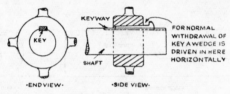

Fig. 45.—Wheel Hub " Keyed " to Shaft.

room allowed for driving the key along the shaft key-way in order to fit it.

A typical gib-head type of key is shown in Fig. 42, and keyways of a shaft are shown in Fig. 43. Fig. 44 shows the hub of a wheel with a key-way, and Fig. 45 a complete and typical assembly of all three components, from which it is hoped the general application will be clearly understood.

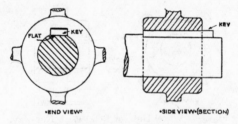

Fig. 46.—Key Bedded on Flat Part of a Shaft.

FLAT KEY (Fig. 46)

A " flat " key is one which, although it is fitted partly into the boss of a wheel or pulley, its lower part does *not* fit *into* the shaft or a shaft key-way of any kind. Instead, it rests on a flat surface which is formed on that portion of the shaft where it is desired to position the wheel-boss.

This type of key is used only where comparatively light loads are concerned, and it is also a less expensive fixture than one which involves the cutting of a key-way in a shaft. A flat key relies on its wedge action for its effect, because, as the wheel commences to rotate, the key is wedged between the flat surface of the shaft and the wheel-boss key-way.

A normal key-way should be formed, extending completely through the boss of the wheel. An assembly of this type of key is shown in Fig. 46.

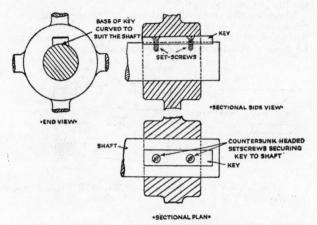

Fig. 47.—" Saddle " Key Secured to Shaft by Set-screws.

SADDLE KEY (Fig. 47)

A " saddle " key is somewhat similar in principle to that just previously described, in so much as it does not fit into a shaft key-way. Furthermore, a saddle key is also used only for work of a light nature, or where it is not subjected to heavy shear stresses.

This type of key, instead of resting on a *flat* surface of the shaft, rests on the *curved* surface. The underside of the key is therefore machined to match the curve of the shaft's circumference, which is also a cheaper proposition than cutting a key-way in the shaft.

In order to attach a saddle key to a shaft, it is securely

held by set-screws which have countersunk heads. This, of course, involves the drilling and "screw-tapping" of the shaft, also the drilling and countersinking of the holes in the key. The number and size of set-screws required for such a fixture depend on the "duty" concerned.

An arrangement of a typical saddle key is shown in the three views in Fig. 47. It will be realised that with such a design it is the set-screws which have to resist the shear stresses, for should they be "sheared off", the wheel and key would continue to rotate on the shaft, while the latter would gradually come to rest.

Therefore the cross-sectional area of the total number of set-screws used must be sufficient to resist the shear stress derived from the power-load concerned, and they must also be made of suitable material to withstand it.

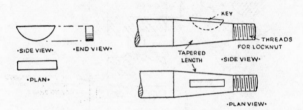

Fig. 48.—A "Woodruff" Key.

Fig. 48a.—"Woodruff" Key Fitted to Shaft.

WOODRUFF KEY (Figs. 48 and 48a)

A further type of key is the "Woodruff". This differs from those previously described in that it is not primarily designed to take the shear stress and is used only for light classes of work.

A Woodruff key is of somewhat "half-moon" shape—in its side view—but is of even width and thickness. It has a curved base, which fits into a similarly shaped recess or key-way in the shaft. This key is mostly used on small shafts or spindles which taper, as shown in Fig. 48a.

The boss of the wheel is also similarly tapered in its "bore" diameter. The wheel is driven on to the shaft along its taper until it fits tightly, so the key is used primarily to locate it, and does not take the shear stress.

In such cases the shaft end is also screw-threaded and

fitted with a nut and washer. After the wheel has been driven on to the shaft (with the key in its relative position) the nut is tightened up hard against the outer face of the boss. This grips the boss and with a wedging action " locks " it securely on the tapered shaft. The key is therefore relieved of the shear stress by the pressure exerted by the nut. This method is extensively adopted for fastening timing-wheels in automobile engines.

A Woodruff key may also be used for parallel shafts where the load is light, but it would then have to resist the shear stress developed.

FEATHER KEY (Fig. 49)

A " feather " key is of rectangular section, and does not taper. It is used by fitting it into the key-way of a shaft, and, unlike a gib-head key, a feather type has no head.

The ends of the key are usually rounded, and it is sunk for about half its depth into the shaft, so that its sides and ends fit snugly all round the key-way recess. Its base should also fit flat on that of the key-way, in which the key should be a good tight fit. The purpose is to provide for a " sliding " movement of the wheel.

It will be seen that a feather key is not used for tightly securing the wheel in a fixed position, but it *does* provide for taking the shear stress, in a similar way to that of a tightly " keyed " wheel-boss. In engineering work it is often desirable to form such a sliding arrangement in order to move a wheel along a shaft to engage or " mesh " it with another fitted to a shaft running parallel with the first.

This arrangement is the principle of gear-box construction, where, in order to obtain the various gear ratios, a certain wheel must be moved along a shaft to engage with another, yet the wheel must be keyed to that shaft in order to rotate or drive it.

An elementary application of this sliding movement is shown in Fig. 49, in which " loose " collars are shown retained by set-screws in the desired " stop " position of the wheel. The collars are positioned where required to ensure that the wheel, when it is moved from one position to another, engages correctly with its " mating " wheel.

In order to effect the sliding movement, the wheel-boss must, of course, be made a working clearance fit on the shaft. The collars therefore safeguard the wheel from sliding off the key at its ends.

In order to more effectively fasten a feather key in its key-way of the shaft, it is sometimes held by two or more counter-sunk-headed set-screws, in a similar manner to that shown in Fig. 47. In some instances, however, the use of a feather key has been superseded by what are known as " splines " formed integrally on the shaft.

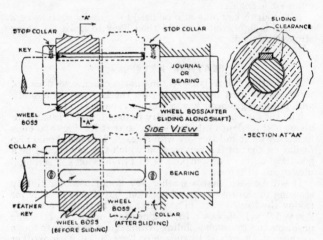

Fig. 49.—Application of " Feather " Key.

SPLINED SHAFT (Figs. 50 and 50a)

In order to attain a similar sliding movement to that already described for a feather key, a shaft is sometimes recessed all around its circumference. The formations in between the recesses thus form projections similar to small keys, as shown in Fig. 50.

If the internal surface of a wheel is similarly shaped, its recesses will fit the relative projections of the mating-shaft, provided a slight working clearance is allowed. Thus, instead of the shaft being fitted with one large key, it has a large number of small " keys " all around it. Collectively these keys, or projections, are designed to be strong enough to resist the shear force involved.

Although such a " splined " formation on a shaft is not,

strictly speaking, a key in the ordinary sense of the term, it is a means of achieving the desired sliding movement of a feather key.

The splined shaft is used extensively for lathes and gear-

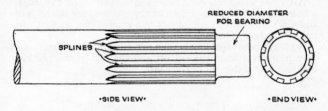

Fig. 50.—Splined Shaft (Square Type " Splines ").

boxes of all descriptions. It is also used for " claw-type " couplings in mechanical engineering work.

Sometimes, however, the splines, instead of being rect-angular in cross-section, are of the V formation, similar to those shown in Fig. 50a. Splines of this type are often fitted

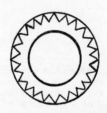

•END VIEW•

Fig. 50a.—" V " Splined Shaft.

to the wheel-hubs of motor-cars, especially those of the racing kinds, for by using such a fixture the wheels are efficiently secured to the axle-shafts, yet can be quickly detached for tyre changing, etc., by " unlocking " a nut from the shaft end and sliding the wheel off the splines.

C

PIN KEY (Fig. 50b)

Another key which is sometimes used, although not so common as those previously mentioned, is the " pin " type. It is a somewhat cheaper system of securing the boss of a wheel to the *end* of a shaft, as shown in Fig. 50b.

After the wheel has been driven into position on the shaft, a hole of suitable size is drilled at the place where the edge of the shaft joins the inner face of the wheel-bore, so that one half of the hole is in each component.

A plain round steel key is then driven tightly into the hole. Any projecting length is cut off and the end of the pin key filed flush with the end of the shaft.

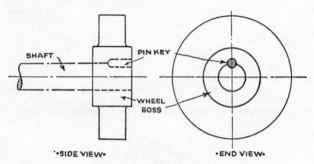

•SIDE VIEW•   •END VIEW•

Fig. 50b.—" Pin " Key Securing Wheel to Shaft End.

This type of key is sometimes used in conjunction with a " shrunk-on " wheel-boss. By this is meant that the wheel-boss is bored out to exactly the same nominal diameter as that of the shaft, instead of a clearance fit being made. The wheel-boss is then heated, in order to expand it, and, whilst still hot, it is driven on to the shaft. As the wheel " cools off ", it " contracts ", and in so doing " grips " tightly on to the shaft. In order to provide extra security, a pin key is often fitted.

Although other special keys may be encountered in engineering, the foregoing are mainly used, of which the rectangular tapered gib-head is possibly the most popular, especially for heavy classes of work.

CHAPTER IV
RIVETS AND RIVETING

(Figs. 51 and 52)

RIVETS are the components used for permanently fastening together articles such as steel plates for boiler construction or sheet-metal tank construction. In general shape or form

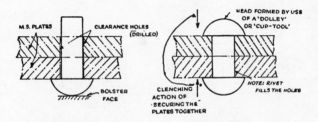

Fig. 51.—Cup (or Snap) Head-Rivet in Position for Riveting.

Fig. 52.—Completed Rivet.

a rivet somewhat resembles a cup-headed bolt, except that it has no screw-threads on its shank.

Rivets are chiefly made of iron or soft steel, but for some purposes, especially for small work, they may be made of copper, brass or aluminium. The last-named material, especially in alloy form, is extensively used for modern aircraft work.

Riveting is carried out either by the " hot " or " cold " process. For rivet sizes of up to approximately 7·937500 mm. ($\frac{5}{16}$ inch) diameter riveting can be done by the cold method, but for work of above that size it is invariably done by the hot method. Cold riveting is usually carried out by " hand-hammering " the plain rivet-shank end in order to form the " clenching " head.

67

"Hot" riveting can be executed either by the hand-hammering principle, or by hydraulic or pneumatic-operated hand-tools or machines. After placing a rivet through the holes of the plates to be fastened together, the head must be firmly supported and pressed close up to the work. This can be effected by using a "bolster"-tool which has a recess in it of similar shape to that of the rivet head. This must in turn be pressed or supported firmly against the rivet, or rested on a solid steel block (see Figs. 51, 63a and 63b).

The rivet shank projects through the holes of the work, and these holes are of slightly larger diameter than that of the rivet, in order to facilitate its positioning. This applies especially to "hot" rivets, which expand slightly on being heated. After the rivet has been placed in position, the work of forming the "closing" head can be commenced.

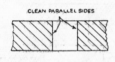

Fig. 53.—Plate Having a "Drilled" Hole.

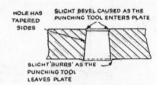

Fig. 54.—Plate With "Punched" Hole.

At the start of the hammering action the first tendency is for the rivet body, in the process of being "compressed", to swell out so as to completely fill the holes, thus filling up the clearance spaces.

As the hammering proceeds, the head formation develops. In order to complete the head formation a "snap", "dolley", or "cupping"-tool is then applied, as shown in Fig. 60. For "cold" riveting, this tool can be held in the hand, similarly to a chisel, as it is struck with the hammer. For "hot" riveting the snap or dolley is applied from the start, but it is then held by a wooden shaft or hazel-twigs, which are lapped around its body.

Note.—The various tools for hand riveting are fully described and illustrated in Volume I, Chapter VIII.

During the "hot"-riveting process, and during the head formation, the rivet gradually cools off, and in so doing it contracts lengthways. The contraction, coupled with the hammering, clenches the plates securely together.

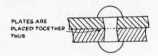

Fig. 55.—Typical Riveted Joint Formed by " Punched " Plate-holes.

This clenching is not so effective with " cold " riveting, which is only developed from the compressive action resulting

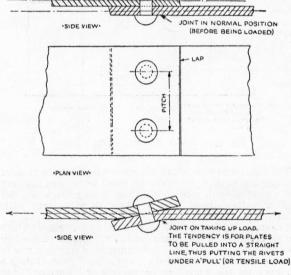

Fig. 56.—Single Riveted " Lap " Joint.

from the hammer-blows. It is because of this that the rivet must be firmly supported at its opposite end. The result achieved by the " hot " formation of a rivet head should be similar to the shape shown in Fig. 52.

Originally the holes formed in plates for riveting work were " punched " out, but, owing to the punching-tool damaging the edges of the holes, this practice has been almost entirely superseded by drilling, which does no damage (see Figs. 53, 54 and 55). The drilling method is absolutely imperative for all boiler work and high-pressure vessels, such as compressed-air " receivers ", etc. Punched holes may still be used for work of less importance, such as feed-chutes for machines, storage hoppers, etc.

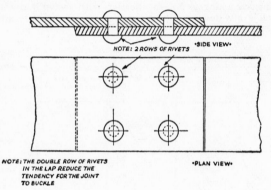

NOTE: 2 ROWS OF RIVETS   •SIDE VIEW•

NOTE: THE DOUBLE ROW OF RIVETS
IN THE LAP REDUCE THE
TENDENCY FOR THE JOINT
TO BUCKLE

•PLAN VIEW•

Fig. 57.—Double Riveted " Lap " Joint.

The punching process may originally have been the cheaper and quicker method, especially for small workshops not very well equipped with modern multiple drilling machines, but with a well-equipped modern plant there is very little difference in the costs.

The duty which rivets are called upon to perform is to take the shear stress of the joints, whilst the plates themselves take the " tensile " stress. Consequently, if only one row of rivets is used in what is called a " single-lap " joint, there is a tendency for the " lap " to be stressed or " buckled " and pulled into a straight line, thus also developing a pull in the rivets. As the rivets were never intended for such a stress, the heads may " fly off " under the pulling or tension force—if it is great—and the joint may thus fail (see Fig. 56). For high-class riveting work, therefore, either a double row of rivets for a single lap joint should be used, or another joint such as a " butt " type should be employed (see Figs. 57 and 58).

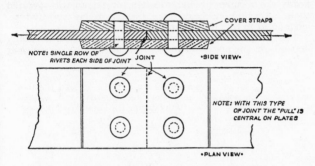

Fig. 58.—Single Riveted " Butt " Joint Using Two Cover Straps.

In addition to the cup-head type of rivet, several other formations are often employed. These are illustrated in Fig. 59.

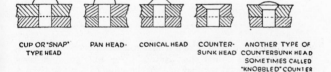

Fig. 59.—Types of Rivet Heads.

Rivets are used extensively for connecting together all classes of rolled metal plates or sections, also various alloys, but it is not usual to rivet " castings ", especially those of " cast " iron, which, being of a brittle nature, are liable to crack or break during the riveting process.

For certain classes of work copper rivets are often used, and for special jobs rivets are sometimes " galvanised " (given a coating of hot zinc) as a precaution against corrosion.

Aluminium-alloy rivets, which are used for aircraft production, are often riveted by the " cold " method. Their heads are formed by light electric or pneumatic-operated tools. Aluminium, being of a comparatively soft nature, lends itself to this procedure.

The particular size of rivets used for each job naturally depends on the plate thickness, together with the distance at

To obtain a neat finished head the tool may be tilted slightly, and worked around during the hammering process.

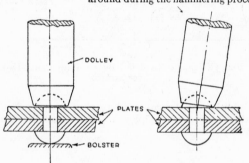

Fig. 60.—Forming the Cup Head.

which they are spaced apart. The space between the centres of two rivets is called the " pitch " (see Fig. 56). A rivet should never be positioned nearer the edge of a plate than a *minimum* of one and a half times its diameter, or the plate is liable to " split " outwards.

When the special cupping tool (snap or dolley) is not available, small work can be hand riveted by using the " ball-pein " of a hand hammer (see Figs. 63a and 63b). No special tool is required for the countersunk rivet head shown in Fig. 59, but a dolley is invariably used for all other large " hot " riveting work. (See Volume I, Figs. 104 and 105.)

USE OF CAULKING TOOL (Fig. 61)

However carefully boiler-plates or pressure tanks may be riveted, they may not always be gas- or water-tight at their joints. As a safeguard against possible leakage, the plate edges near the joints may be " caulked " by the use of this tool.

Caulking is the process of forcing the edges of the plates very closely together, by using the tool and a hand-hammer in a similar way to that of a " cold " chisel and hammer. This action somewhat " thickens " up the lap plate edge, and causes it to " bite " into the adjacent plate, thus forming a leak-proof joint.

In many instances the edges of rivet heads are also caulked in order to procure a more efficient " seal ". This is done by gradually working the tool all round the rivet edges as it is struck by the hammer.

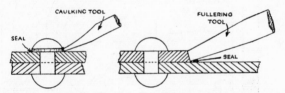

Fig. 61.—" Caulking "   Fig. 62.—" Fullering " a Riveted
      a Rivet.   Plate-edge.

"FULLERING " (Fig. 62)

Another method of more effectively sealing the edges of plates is the use of a " fullering tool ". This is somewhat similar to a caulking tool, but of stouter and more robust construction. The thickness of its blade is equal to that of the plate edge.

When fullering of joints is anticipated, the edge of the lap plate should previously be " chamfered " or " sloped " as shown in Fig. 62. After placing the tool edge firmly against that of the plate edge, the former is struck by a heavy hammer and gradually moved across the full extent of the plate's edge. This results in a thickening of the lap edge, which is forced closer to the lower plate.

A further use for a rivet is to form a swivel " hinge-pin ", as applied to a " swing-type " cover-plate on machinery. In such a case a washer is usually placed between the cover and the work to form a distance-piece, and the rivet is " cold "-riveted up, but not too tightly, as this would prevent the cover-plate being moved. Such an application is shown in Fig. 63.

COLD " HAND "-TYPE RIVETING (Figs. 63a and 63b)

For all classes of " cold " hand riveting work the object should be to effect a head resembling as near as possible that of a " machine " or snap formed head. With a little care

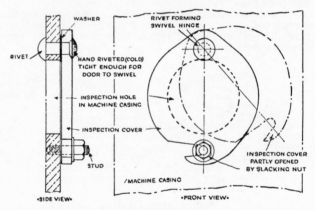

Fig. 63.—Rivet and Washer Used to Form Swivel-hinge for Inspection Cover-plate.

quite good results can be obtained by using a ball-pein type hand hammer. It chiefly depends on the skill of the operator.

For good, neat results the work should be rigidly supported, and rivets of the correct length must be used. If the rivet shank is too long, and projects too far through the work, the resulting head will be " bulky ". If too short, it will be found impossible to form a properly shaped head, and the head thus formed will be too flat. The correct length will soon be found by trial.

The rivet should not be hammered down too flat, and each hammer-blow should be at a different position. This is best effected by gradually working around the rivet as evenly as possible. The force of each blow should also be even and regular.

It is preferable to strike a large number of light blows rather than a few less in number but of greater force. At the start of the operation the head should be " roughly " formed, then as the shape develops the small " dents " and " lumps " can be gradually beaten out, so as to form a fully defined head. The process should be continued, the aim being to diminish any high " spots " which remain by lightly striking each as the work is " gone over " to complete it.

A novel rivet worthy of note is the " explosive " type. This is used for special light classes of work, and is made of

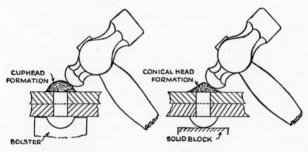

Fig. 63a.   Fig. 63b.

Hand Riveting.

aluminium alloy. Inside its shank, near the plain end, is a small " explosive charge ". These rivets are used for work where the outside surface only is accessible, such as those of small cylindrical shape, aeroplane metal wings, etc., the internal surface of which is inaccessible to normal riveting tools.

After placing the rivet *from outside the work*, its cup-head is heated (an electric soldering iron is often used for the purpose). Heat is conducted along the rivet-shank and explodes the charge, which " bulges out " that end of the shank, thus forming a head.

CHAPTER V

SHAFTS, COLLARS, CRANKS, ECCENTRIC, ETC. (GENERAL)

SHAFT (PLAIN ROUND TYPE) (Fig. 64)

A " SHAFT " is the name of the component on which are mounted pulleys, gear-wheels, etc., forming the axle upon which they can rotate. A shaft is mounted in bearings in order to locate and support it, and in most cases it is made of steel. It is usually of solid cylindrical shape, but in some instances may be of square cross-section, with only its ends of cylindrical shape, in order that the latter may fit into the bearings. A shaft may also be of hollow construction. A " thin " or " light " type of shaft is often referred to as a " spindle ".

In addition to their being used for carrying gear-wheels or pulleys, shafts are used for other purposes, such as the mounting of the propeller for a ship or aeroplane. In the latter instances the propeller would be mounted at one end of the shaft. Furthermore, the plain or " toothed " rollers of crushing and grinding machinery are mounted on shafts. A bicycle wheel rotates on a shaft, or spindle, so do the cycle pedals and cranks.

From the above examples it will be appreciated that a shaft, when in use, is subjected to a " *twist* " or " *torsional* " stress, as it is termed. The shaft must therefore be of ample strength to resist such a stress.

Referring to the shaft with pulleys mounted on it, as shown in Fig. 64, the pulleys are driven by belts. In order to rotate the smaller pulley there must be a pull on one side of it exerted by the belt. Let it be assumed that this pulley is driven from an engine. The larger pulley on the shaft is possibly used for transmitting the motive-power to some machine, therefore in its belt there will also be a pull exerted. These two pulls will transmit " loads " on to the shaft, which tend to " bend " it, and the weights of the pulleys themselves also tend to bend it. It will be realised, therefore, that the shaft must be of sufficient strength to resist the bending stresses involved, in addition to the twisting stress previously referred to.

From the foregoing explanations it will be seen that a shaft requires careful design and consideration, as it must be of sufficient size and strength to withstand the various loads applied to it.

If a shaft sags or bends under its loading, additional and unintentional stresses are also transmitted to the bearings in which it rotates. In due course such a practice would cause the bearings to fail.

The arrangement of a shaft, complete with its bearings and

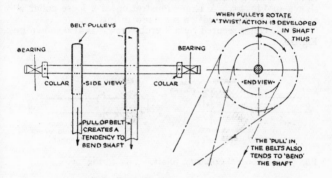

Fig. 64.—Shaft Fitted With Pulleys Showing " Bending " and " Twisting " Stresses Developed.

pulleys, as illustrated in Fig. 64, is called a " line-shaft " or " counter-shaft ".

The metal from which shafts are made varies in quality with the duty which it is called upon to perform. They may be of solid or tubular steel, and their outer surfaces are machined to the required diameters in a " lathe ". The keyways are also cut out by machine. For high-class " finish " they are accurately " ground " on their surfaces.

Note.—Volume III introduces " lathe work ".

LOOSE COLLARS ON SHAFT (Figs. 65 and 17)

In the case of a plain round shaft of even diameter, such as that shown in Fig. 64, some method of preventing it moving longitudinally must be used.

In order to locate it, and prevent any side movement, loose " thrust-collars " are employed. One loose collar is shown positioned on the inner face of each of the two bearings. The " collars " are plain, short, hollow cylinders, and are fixed in the desired positions by set-screws. Loose thrust-collars are usually made of steel or cast iron.

If the boss of a pulley or gear-wheel can be conveniently positioned adjacent to the face of a bearing, however, it is only necessary to fit one loose collar at the other end of the bearing, for the wheel-boss, being " keyed " to the shaft, thus provides a fixing. Such an application as the above is shown in Fig. 65. A larger illustration of a loose collar is also shown complete with a set-screw in Fig. 17.

A loose collar secured by a " grub-screw " is also shown in Fig. 29.

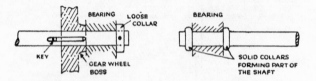

Fig. 65.—" Loose " Collar on Shaft.   Fig. 66.

Such collars are given an easy " sliding " fit on their shafts to faciliate their being moved along easily in order to position them. The set-screws should be securely tightened in order to prevent them from working loose.

It is not essential to fit loose collars at the *inner* faces of the bearings; they may be fitted to the ends of the shaft at the outer faces.

SOLID COLLARS ON SHAFTS (Fig. 66)

As an alternative to the use of loose collars, in certain instances solid collars may be used which are formed integral with the shaft. These types, being of rigid construction, locate a shaft perfectly, and cannot of course work loose. A disadvantage is that the bearing must be assembled over the shaft, so it is essential for the former to be of the split type.

A shaft fitted with loose thrust-collars can be inserted through a " one-piece " or plain " bushed " bearing, and the collars can at the same time be conveniently fitted and " slid " along the shaft, and finally positioned by screwing up their set-screws.

Shafts on which are formed " solid "-type collars cost more to produce because they must be made either by " forging " them or by machining from a solid shaft of larger diameter. They are preferable, however, for certain jobs.

"SHOULDERS" ON SHAFTS (Fig. 67)

In certain cases it may be found necessary for a shaft to be of a specified diameter to withstand the various " torsional " and bending stresses, but it might not be essential to maintain the same diameter throughout the shaft's length. It may therefore be advisable to reduce the

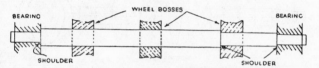

Fig. 67.—Shaft with " Shoulders."

diameter in certain parts, especially at the ends which fit into the bearings.

The cost of the extra machining work involved in the reduction process would probably be " offset " by the ability to fit bearings of a smaller diameter, these being less expensive than those of larger sizes. The places at which the alteration in the diameter of the shaft occurs are called " shoulders ". A further advantage of forming a shoulder on a shaft is that it automatically forms a " stop ", equivalent to a collar, against which the boss-face of a wheel can be positioned. Typical shoulders are shown in Fig. 67.

CRANK-SHAFT (Fig. 68)

A " crank-shaft " is a special form of shaft designed to convert rotary motion to reciprocating type. It is used extensively in engine or pump construction, and has off-sets called " cranks " positioned at certain distances from its centre line.

The cranks are formed so as to enable " connecting-rods " to be attached, which allow the pistons to maintain reciprocating motion in their respective cylinders. The distance from the shaft centre-line to the " crank-pin " centre is called the " throw ". A crank-shaft, having one throw only, is often used in machine construction in conjunction with a single connecting-rod in order to provide a reciprocating motion for another part of the machine.

Engine crank-shafts are formed either from steel " drop forgings ", which have their wearing surfaces machined, or accurately ground, or may be made by their being " cast " from special " alloy " steels, and their moving parts ground to give a fine " finish ".

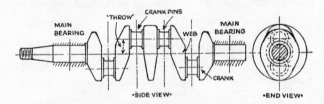

Fig. 68.—Engine Crank-shaft (Machined from a Solid Forging).

CAMSHAFT (Fig. 68a)

This is another form of special shaft. It is one of straight form which has humps or " cams " formed integrally. The cams may be of varying shape, depending on the nature of the work for which it is required.

A camshaft is used extensively for operating the valves of internal-combustion engines. A typical camshaft used for such purposes is shown in Fig. 68a. The cam formations are usually of pear-shape form, and their " peaks " are set at varying angles to suit the " timing " of the valves. These angles constitute the " harmonic " of the cam. The surfaces of the cams are usually " case-hardened ", in order better to resist the wear.

The application of a camshaft to an engine is that it is so positioned that the cams bear on the respective " tappets ". The latter in turn bear on the valve stems. As the camshaft is rotated by the valve " timing-gear ", the cam peak (or pointed end) lifts the tappet, and the tappet being positioned in between the cam and the valve, the latter is consequently lifted or " opened ", thus regulating the admission or exhaust of the gases.

Camshafts may be machined from solid steel or made by " drop-forging ". Their wearing parts are finally ground to an accurate finish, and the cam surfaces are heat-treated in order to harden them.

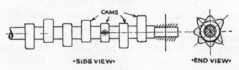

Fig. 68a.—Camshaft (Machined from Solid Bar).

In addition to the pear-shaped cam mentioned above, other forms are often used in engineering. A well-known form is " heart-shaped ". It will be realised that any other predetermined motion can be given to anything attached to the surface of a cam, and which presses against it. If a rod is pressed against a cam, and the former is free to move in a

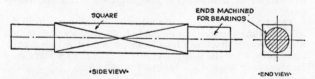

Fig. 69.—Square Shaft (Machined from Solid Square Bar).

guide, it must naturally " trace " out a " path " similar to that traversed by the cam at its point of contact with the rod.

SQUARE SHAFT (Fig. 69)

For certain jobs it is preferable to use shafts of " square " formation. These have their ends " turned " down to circular form in order to accommodate the bearings.

This class of shaft is often used for heavy types of industrial machinery, such as those used for coal-crushers. The "claws" or "rollers" of the "crushers" have square holes in their bosses through which the square part of the shaft is fixed. Such construction obviates the use of keys and keyways.

Shafts of this nature are frequently made from black-type square steel bars, which only require their ends machining to provide for the accommodation of the bearings.

ECCENTRIC SHAFT (Fig. 69a)

An "eccentric" shaft has a centre which is offset from the axis on which it rotates. It is used to give a reciprocating motion to anything mounted upon it. It is very often used to give that kind of motion to the "jaws" of crushing and grinding machinery, and a short eccentric shaft is used

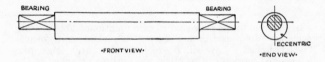

Fig. 69a.—"Eccentric" Shaft (Machined from Solid Bar).

extensively in steam-engine design for operating the valve-gears.

This type of shaft is usually made by machining it from the solid, but may sometimes be made from steel forgings which are afterwards machined true to shape in a lathe. For high-class work, after the machining process, the shaft surface may be accurately ground to obtain a smooth finish.

HOLLOW SHAFT (Fig. 70a)

In order to reduce the weight of a shaft, instead of its being made solid, it is sometimes made "hollow", or of "tubular" formation. Actually, weight for weight, a hollow shaft is stronger than a solid one for resisting the bending stress involved, because of the large diameter of the former. This does *not* mean that if both the hollow and solid shafts are of *equal* outside diameters, their strengths are the same.

The student will appreciate that if an existing 76·200 mm. (3-inch)-diameter shaft is "hollowed out" it will not be stronger than it was previously. It follows, however, that for any given *weight* of material to be used for the construction of a certain shaft, a stronger one could be formed of tubular shape *BUT* of greater diameter than if the *same* weight of the *same* material were used to make a solid shaft.

The principle is allied to what is known as the " Modulus of Section " of the cross-sectional area of the shafts concerned.

Note.—For further information on the property of " Modulus of Section ", the reader is advised to refer to a book on " Applied Mechanics " or one on the " Strength of Materials ".

The hollow construction is often used for shaft design where it is essential to retain strength, combined with weight

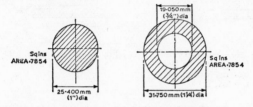

Fig. 70.—Solid Shaft. Fig. 70a.—Hollow Shaft (of same area).

Note.—Both shafts are made from similar material; both have the same cross-sectional areas, yet the hollow one is stronger and better enabled to resist bending stress for equal loading.

reduction. It is the outermost part of a shaft's cross-section from which the strength is derived, and the strength diminishes correspondingly towards the centre-line, or axis. Comparisons, together with diagrams, are given in Figs. 70 and 70a, from which it will be seen that both shafts have the same cross-sectional area, yet the hollow one is much the stronger.

Consideration has only been given so far to shafts which are normally used in horizontal planes, and which rotate in plain bearings or those of the ball-and-roller type, which can easily be lubricated.

VERTICAL SHAFTS (Figs. 71, 72, and 72a)

For certain classes of work " vertical " shafts, or those which rotate whilst in a vertical plane, sometimes have to be used. Although to a great extent the construction of these resembles those already dealt with, special attention has to be paid to their ends and the bearings in which they rotate.

An ordinary plain, round type of vertical shaft is shown in

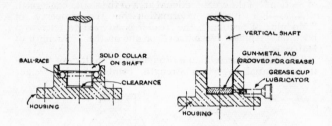

Fig. 71.—Vertical Shaft (supported on Ball-bearings which take the load).

Fig. 72.—Vertical Shaft (supported on G.M. Pad).

Fig. 72. The lower end of such a shaft might be " case-hardened " in order to resist the wear. It would possibly be mounted so as to rest on a " gun-metal " pad, the top face

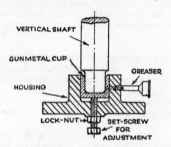

Fig. 72a.—Vertical Shaft (carried in G.M. Cup, and Provided with Adjustment for Wear).

of which would be recessed with " grease-grooves " or " channels ". Such a shaft might be used where the load was of a light nature.

A slightly more elaborate type is shown in Fig. 72a.

In this case it will be noticed the shaft end has been reduced in diameter, and is carried in a gun-metal cup which forms the liner of the bearing. Adjustment for wear is also provided by a stout set-screw with a lock-nut.

Fig. 71, however, shows a more satisfactory design, for in this case the shaft has a solid collar formed integrally with the shaft. The collar is mounted on a " ball-race " of substantial type, and the ball-race is housed in a casting. It will be seen that a clearance is provided between the end of the shaft and the housing. For this type of shaft the wearing face of the collar would probably be case-hardened.

Several types of shafts having been considered, the following conclusions may be arrived at :—

(a) For countershafts or line-shafts, plain round types of mild-steel construction are mostly employed—as in Fig. 64.

(b) For special duties, steel of high quality must be used.

(c) The wearing surfaces of shafts may be case-hardened, or " heat " treated, to enable them to resist wear, as in Figs. 68 and 69a, also 72 and 72a.

Note.—" Case-hardening " is the name applied to a process of giving a " hard " shell to the shafts' surface.

(d) Shafts may be made from solid forgings or from castings, and afterwards their wearing surfaces may be machined or ground—as in Fig. 68.

(e) They may have solid collars formed on them to retain them in position.

(f) Shafts may have " shoulders " formed on them, and certain parts of the same shaft may be of various diameters, etc.

(g) They may also be of square formation along their main parts, and the ends only machined to accommodate the bearings.

(h) Shafts may be either of the splined type or may have keyways in order to fix any component mounted on them.

(i) They may be used in a " horizontal ", " vertical ", or " inclined " plane, depending on the purpose for which they are applied.

(j) They may also be used in spindle form for operating various " mechanisms " by the addition of levers or handwheels, etc.

(k) Shafts can be of equal diameter throughout their lengths, or parts may be tapered, and certain parts may be screw-threaded in order to accommodate " security nuts ", etc.

(*l*) In addition to their being made of steel, shafts may (for special jobs) be constructed of brass or other alloys.

"SPINDLE" (Fig. 72*b*)

This is the name applied to a light class of shaft which is usually of thin and long formation.   A spindle is often used in conjunction with either a hand-lever or a hand-wheel for

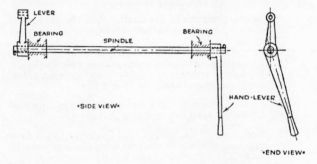

Fig. 72*b*.—Lever " Spindle " (or Light Type Shaft).

operating some mechanism. Fig. 72*b* shows a typical application of a spindle used for forming the " fulcrum " of a system of levers.   Spindles for such jobs are made of mild steel.

CHAPTER VI

COUPLINGS AND CLUTCHES (GENERAL)

A " COUPLING " is the name applied to the component used to connect or " couple " together two lengths of shafting end to end. There are many different forms used in mechanical engineering, some of which are of one-piece construction, while other types may be composed of several parts.

Couplings may perhaps be divided into two groups : those of the fixed or rigid class, usually made of either cast iron or mild steel, and those of the " flexible " type, made partly of metal and partly of rubber, leather, or special compositions of an elastic nature, in order to provide some form of flexibility and to act as a " shock absorber " for the " drive ".

The rigid type of coupling is used in cases where a high degree of lineal alignment is to be provided. The flexible kinds are used where such true alignment cannot be obtained, so they are used in order to allow for " misalignment ", as well as to provide some " cushion " or shock-absorber for the drive.

Couplings of the " claw " or " jaw " type are used to bring into motion a second shaft, which is positioned in the same lineal plane as the first shaft, so that although the latter may be constantly rotating, the second shaft might be required to rotate only occasionally.

Other types of couplings are used in order to connect together two shafts the axes of which may be set at an angle to each other, and are therefore not in a straight line; and some are used as safety measures in order to safeguard the machine (to which it is coupled) from damage due to overloading.

A further type of coupling has a " floating " centrepiece positioned between the two jaw-pieces. This provides a sliding movement during the shafts' rotation, to offset any slight misalignment of the two shafts which it connects. It is used for slow-speed shafts subjected to high " torque " or " twisting ".

A special type of coupling may also be used for connecting shafts of different diameters.

RIGID COUPLINGS

Muff Couplings (Figs. 73 and 74)

A " muff " coupling is of the rigid one-piece type. It is of cylindrical formation, and the centre is " bored " and " key-wayed " to suit the shaft diameter concerned. This kind of coupling is usually made of cast iron, but for heavy-duty

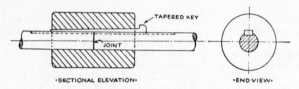

Fig. 73.—" Muff " Coupling (Single Key Type).

work it may be made of steel. Either one long key can be used, as shown in Fig. 73, or two shorter keys, as shown in Fig. 74. If two keys are used, one of them must have no head.

Whenever this type of " keying-up " is carried out, a small space should be left at the shafts' joint position to ensure

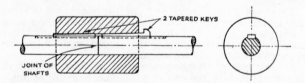

Fig. 74.—" Muff " Coupling (Two Keys Type).

that the second key does not bear on the end of the first, as, if it does, it will not be a good " fit " in the latter part of the coupling. Whichever system of keying-up is used, care must be taken to ensure that the key, or keys, fit or bear well for their entire lengths.

It should be realised that long lengths of shafting, such as " line-shafts " in a works, cannot be made in one piece of indefinite length. Couplings must therefore be used to connect together the individual lengths of shafting. It is very important that the various lengths are " lined-up " or " set " in as straight a line as possible, or undue stress will be " set-up " in the bearings and couplings.

A line-shaft is the long main line of shafting in a works or factory, from which the various drives are taken in order to operate certain machines spaced about the building.   It will be realised that such line-shafting is often subjected to various stresses, as some of the machines are " started " and " stopped " intermittently.   The muff-coupling, having no projections, is a safe type to use in cases of this kind, for it eliminates the liability of workmen having their arms or clothing caught in it whilst oiling bearings, etc.

Split-type Muff Coupling (Fig. 75)

This type of coupling—as its name implies—is split longitudinally in two halves, and the joint faces are machined.

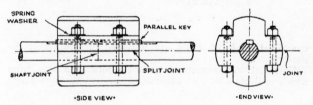

Fig. 75.—" Muff " Coupling (Split Type).

The key used with this coupling is of parallel formation, there being no need for a " taper " fit, as the bolts secure and " clamp " the two halves tightly together.   Dismantling is greatly facilitated with this sort of coupling, as, by simply unbolting, it can easily be removed from the shaft.

It is recommended that whenever possible couplings should be positioned adjacent to the bearings of the shafts concerned, because were they positioned midway between two bearings some distance apart, certain undue stress, due to the weight of the coupling when it is rotated, would be set up in the shaft, which might cause it to " whip " or bend.   This, in due course, would affect the bearings and cause unnecessary wear.

Flanged Coupling (Fig. 76)

The " flanged " coupling is used extensively.   It is usually made of cast iron, but is sometimes made of steel.   It is made in two halves, with the joint formed at right angles to the axis of the shafts. The joint faces are accurately

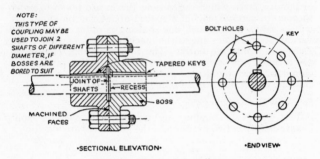

·SECTIONAL ELEVATION·   ·END VIEW·

Fig. 76.—Flanged Coupling.

machined, and bolt-holes are provided, as shown in the illustration.

Each half of the coupling takes the form of a boss, from which projects a flange of circular formation through which

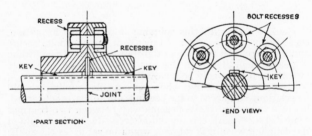

·PART SECTION·   ·END VIEW·

Fig. 76a.—Flanged Coupling (with Recesses for Bolts).

are bolt-holes—spaced equidistant as shown. Each half-coupling is securely keyed to the end of each shaft by tapered keys, and the flanges are then bolted together.

For high-class work the coupling is sometimes machined all

over, and bright bolts are fitted. For work of less importance only the bores of the bosses, the keyways, and the faces of the joint flanges are machined. The latter are sometimes provided with a recess, especially if the coupling is made of cast iron, as this reduces the area of the flange-faces to be machined. Bolts of the black type would be used.

Some flanged couplings, instead of having their bolt-heads and nuts projecting from the flanges, have recesses at the bolt-hole positions, as shown in Fig. 76a. Here the nuts and bolt-heads do *not* form projections, which therefore reduces the risk of accidents to workmen.

With this type of coupling the shear stresses involved are shared between the keys and the bolts.

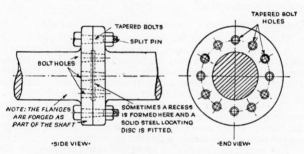

Fig. 77.—Solid Flange Coupling (Marine Type).

A coupling of this kind can be used to join together two shafts of different diameter by boring out the bosses to suit each relative shaft diameter.

Solid Flange Coupling—Marine Type (Fig. 77)

Another means of forming a junction between two shafts is to forge their ends so as to form a flange on each. This practice is adopted extensively for marine work, and is applied to ship propeller-shafts. This coupling, which is an integral part of the shaft, is machined all over its surface.

In most cases tapered bolts of high-quality steel of the bright type are used. The nuts are often of the " castellated " pattern, fitted with split pins. In some cases a " recess " is formed centrally in each flange face, into which is fitted a solid steel machined " locating-disc ", as shown in the illustration.

Owing to the arduous duty which ship propeller-shafts are called upon to perform, they are consequently made of very good quality steel. Sometimes, more especially for the larger shaft sizes, instead of being solid they are made hollow, for the reason previously explained in regard to Fig. 70a. This is in order to reduce the weight of the shaft and at the same time to increase its strength, the better to enable it to resist the bending and torsion stresses. In order to provide " *dead true* " alignment it is necessary for the faces of the coupling flanges to be machined or ground to a very high degree of accuracy.

Marine shafts of the above description are often made up to 20 inches in diameter, and thus require coupling flanges of massive construction.

Universal Coupling or " Hooke's Joint " (Figs. 78 and 78a)

This is a special coupling or joint which is employed for the connection of two shaft-ends, each set at an angle to the other, and the angle of inclination can be varied whilst the shafts are actually rotating. This principle has been applied extensively to automobile propeller-shafts which permit the back axle to move up or down when traversing uneven roads.

The engine-power is thus transmitted via the gear-box and propeller-shaft to the back axle during the up or downward movement of the latter, owing to the movement of the axle suspension springs due to a road's unevenness.

The same principle is also made use of in certain cases for general mechanical engineering where two shafts have to be connected together and their axes intersect at an angle to each other.

The coupling is often made of steel, " malleable iron ", or drop-forgings, and comprises a central " lug-piece ", the ends of which are drilled or bored at right angles to each other, in order to accommodate a " hinge-pin " in each of the drilled holes. Attached to each pin is a " fork-shaped " boss which is secured to the shaft's end.

The bosses are either keyed to the shafts, or the latter may be screw-threaded into the bosses and secured by a driven pin passing through both the shaft and the boss. The pin's ends are then " burred " or riveted over. The hinge-pins are made of steel, and their surfaces are often case-hardened in order to resist wear.

For high-class work these pins are drilled centrally and fitted with lubricators and grease or oil-groove " channels ",

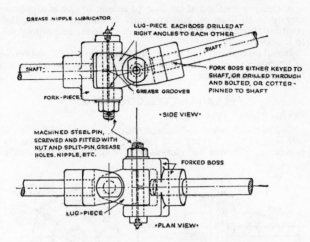

Fig. 78.—Universal Coupling (Assembled).

because it is at the pin positions that wear takes place owing to the constant movement during use. The hinge-pins are

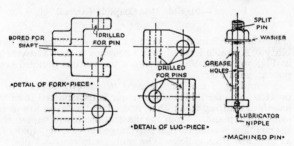

Fig. 78a.—Coupling Details.

usually screw-threaded and fitted with nuts and split pins, as shown in the illustration of Fig. 78a.

A cheaper method than that of fitting a grease-nipple is merely to drill an oil-hole centrally in the lug-piece at the position through which the hinge-pin passes, and apply oil to it occasionally.

It will be realised that as the lug-piece forms the " swivel " or hinge upon which the whole coupling works, some form of lubrication is necessary.

FLEXIBLE-TYPE COUPLINGS

Flexible " Disc " Type (Fig. 79)

One of the simplest and most common forms of a " flexible " coupling is that having a " yielding " element between its jaw-faces. Rubber and canvas bonded together is frequently

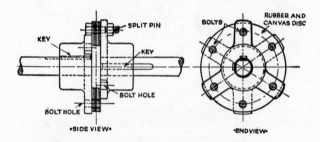

Fig. 79.—Flexible Disc Coupling (Assembled).

the " element " used, on account of its elasticity and flexibility. A simple form of such a coupling is shown assembled in Fig. 79, whilst Fig. 79a shows the various detailed components separately.

A coupling of this kind is used to absorb " shock " or to provide some flexibility when power is transmitted from one length of shafting to another, and when the latter are in the same lineal plane. From the illustrations it will be seen that the coupling is composed of two flanged bosses, or " spiders ", as they are often called. The rubber and canvas " disc " is bolted to the " *diagonally opposite* " flanges, as will be seen in the end view of Fig. 79, which shows the flanges of the rear " spider " in dotted lines.

The flexibility is thus obtained because the " spider "-flanges of one shaft are bolted to the disc, *BUT* at different positions from those of the other shaft. The disc will obviously " give " or yield as power is transmitted from one shaft to the other.

The disc illustrated is composed of alternate layers of rubber and canvas, which are " vulcanised " or bonded together. Other types of discs are occasionally used. These are sometimes formed of leather which has been previously treated with tallow to make it more pliable and to preserve it. Other discs are composed of a series of very thin " spring-steel " laminations which bend slightly during use. Whichever type of disc is used to form this kind of flexible coupling, all conform to the same principle of being enabled to yield between the bolted positions.

The flanged bosses, or " spiders ", are usually made of

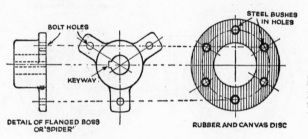

Fig. 79a.—Coupling Components.

cast iron, but may sometimes be formed of drop-forgings or malleable iron. The coupling bolts are made of steel, and those of bright type are mainly used especially for high-class jobs.

This coupling is suitable either for " slow " or " fast " revolving shafts.

Belt and Pin Type Coupling (Fig. 80)

This coupling provides flexibility, and caters also for the slight misalignment of the two shafts concerned. It is composed of two flanged bosses, but in this instance the flanges have steel " pins " projecting from them, as shown in the " assembly " view of the illustration.

The pins are rigidly fixed into the flanges, and are evenly spaced in " circular formation " at a certain distance from the centre of one flange, but at a different distance in the case of the other flange. A flat endless leather belt " weaves "

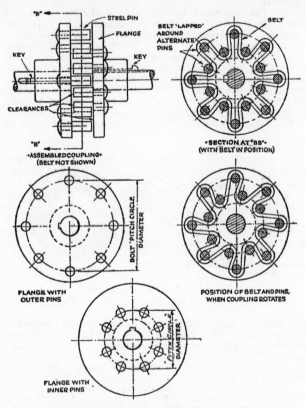

Fig. 80.—Looped Belt and Pin Type Coupling.

over the pins, thus forming " loops ", as shown in the section " BB " view of the diagram.

As the driving-shaft is rotated, the coupling-flange to which it is attached also rotates, and in so doing changes the position of its pins relative to those of the driven coupling-flange. During this relative " change " the shape of the " loop formation " is altered, due to the sluggishness of the driven flange in commencing to rotate. This sluggishness therefore provides a certain flexibility, due to the driven flange tending to lag behind the driving one until its loops become tight.

Referring again to the illustration of the assembled coupling, it will be noticed that the pins of one flange do not make contact with the face of the opposite flange, and that a clearance is consequently provided between those parts.

The belt *width* is also slightly *less* than the distance between the inner faces of the two flanges. By this means provision is made for the misalignment of the shafts, because the two flanges are not directly or rigidly connected. They are connected only through the medium of the *belt*, which is looped over the pins of each coupling flange. The belt, being of a flexible nature, provides a certain amount of " yield " between the flanges, and in so doing compensates for any slight misalignment.

The flanges are usually made of steel or malleable iron, and the pins are of steel construction. In some cases the pins, instead of being riveted in position (as shown in the illustration), are screw-threaded and fitted with nuts and split-pins. For high-class jobs, and in order to reduce wear on the belt, the pins can be fitted with freely rotating " rollers " or " sleeves ", over which the belt can move easily, thus reducing friction.

This coupling is suitable for use with slowly rotating shafts.

Flexible Coupling (Coil-spring Type) (Figs. 81a to 81e)

There are several kinds of flexible couplings which make use of steel " coil " or " helical " compression springs in order to form the " yielding " element.

Most of these are similar in their basic principles, but the application of the springs differs slightly. The type illustrated in the various diagrams of Figs. 81a, b, c, d, and e comprises two flanged bosses of the orthodox coupling pattern, and generally similar to those of the type previously described in Fig. 80. The coupling at present under consideration, however, has " jaws " or " teeth " evenly spaced, which project from the flanges' inner faces. The jaws are of tapered formation as depicted in Fig. 81c.

Fig. 81a shows the complete assembly of the coupling, from which it will be seen the " half-coupling " " *A* " is

D

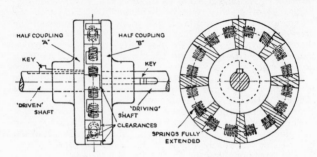

Fig. 81a.

Fig. 81b.

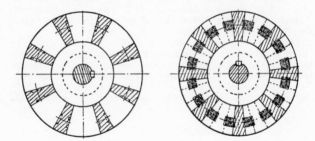

Fig. 81c.

Fig. 81d.

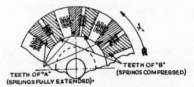

Fig. 81e.

Coil-spring Type Coupling.

attached to the driven shaft, and the "mating" half-coupling " B " is keyed to the driving-shaft.

Fig. 81b shows half-coupling " A " with the coil-springs fitted to its jaws. These are held in the flanges by bolts or set-screws. The "mating" half-coupling " B " (shown in Fig. 81c) has no springs, but its jaws have recesses in which to accommodate the projecting spring-ends of " A ". These are shown together with the jaws of both " A " and " B " in " mesh ", or " interlocked ", with the extended springs positioned between the flanges in Fig. 81d.

When the driving-shaft—to which " B " is attached—is rotated, pressure is exerted on the springs tending to " compress " or " close up " their coils. As the pressure is increased the spring-coils become totally closed up, and consequently form the equivalent of solid " buffers ". The pressure is thus transmitted to the jaws of " A ", which in due course rotates. Although the process of compressing the springs and transmitting the pressure to the jaws of " A " is of a momentary nature only, the shock is absorbed during this " starting-up " process, which eliminates the harshness of the drive.

In Fig. 81a it will be noticed that clearances are shown between the jaw projections of half-coupling " A " and the inner face of " B " flange. These clearances, together with the flexibility of the springs, provide for any slight misalignment of the shafts. Usually a cover-strap is attached to one of the half-coupling flanges, which totally encloses the springs and jaws.

This coupling can be " reversed ", or operated successfully in either direction of rotation.

Fig. 81e shows the positions adopted by the jaws of each half-coupling and the springs of " A " when flange " B " is driving " A " in the direction of the arrow.

It will be appreciated that the springs thus form " cushions " which gradually absorb the " shock " transmitted from the drive of the motive power used.

Fluid Coupling or Hydraulic Type (Fig. 82)

The fluid or " hydraulic " coupling is perhaps one of the most modern kinds, and is rapidly gaining popularity. Of recent years it has been developed and used extensively in the automobile industry in connection with what has been termed " fluid flywheel " drive. Its principles have been widely adopted for general mechanical engineering work.

In general principle the " fluid coupling " consists of two main parts : an " impeller " " A " (a disc fitted with radial

" vanes ") which is fitted to and rotated by the driving-shaft, and a " runner " " *B* " of similar construction, which is secured to the driven shaft.

The two parts are mounted in a casing sealed by a metal-to-metal gland, as shown in the sectional view of Fig. 82, the coupling being filled with oil to a pre-determined level. There is no mechanical connection between the impeller and the runner, except for the ball bearings which carry the driven shaft.

When the driving-shaft carrying the impeller is rotated,

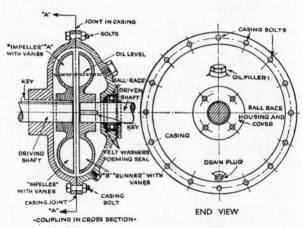

Fig. 82.—Fluid Type Coupling (Principle of).

the " blades " or " vanes " cause the oil to circulate, due to centrifugal force, the oil being—as it were—pumped on to the vanes of the runner, which acts like a turbine. When the velocity of the oil is sufficient to overcome the resistance to rotation of the runner, the runner commences to rotate.

The torque transmitted builds up as the square of the speed of the impeller and, as there is no mechanical connection between the impeller and the runner, but simply a vortex ring of oil, the acceleration is extremely smooth.

So long as the impeller is rotated the oil continues to circulate, and at normal speed and load the " slip ", or difference in speed between the impeller and runner, is about 2% to 3%, *i.e.* the efficiency of the coupling is about 97% to 98%. The fact that the runner is rotating slower than the impeller means that the centrifugal pressure of oil at the entry to the runner will be less than at the exit from the impeller, thus determining the flow of oil through the vanes. The rate of acceleration can be varied over a considerable range by increasing or decreasing the amount of oil in the coupling.

It will be realised by the student that one great advantage of a fluid coupling is that the slip provides a safety measure for the machine which it is driving and, furthermore, the

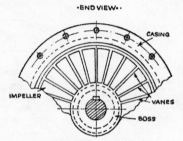

Fig. 82a.—Enlarged Part Section at " AA " (showing " Impeller " Vanes).

Note.—Runner vanes are similar.

torque transmitted can be limited to a predetermined amount in the event of the runner shaft being stalled. Under such conditions of maximum slip the vortex ring of oil circulates rapidly until the obstruction is removed, and the runner then accelerates up to speed.

In the case of internal combustion engines, the fluid coupling prevents the engine from being stalled.

Other advantages of this type of coupling include the ability, in many cases, to use simpler and cheaper types of electrical motors and switch gear. Also, in drives where the starting torque is higher than the running torque, it is usually possible to rate the motor for the running condition rather than the starting, due to the fact that the fluid coupling permits a light load start.

Fig. 82a shows an enlarged part section of the impeller or runner vanes.

Shear-bolt Coupling (Fig. 83)

In its strictest sense this is actually more in the nature of a safety device than an ordinary coupling. Unlike those previously described, a " shear-bolt " coupling is not used merely to join two shafts together. Its primary object is to provide a safeguard should the machine to which it is attached become inadvertently " overloaded ", clogged, or choked by a foreign obstruction gaining access to its mechanism.

As its name implies, the coupling is composed of one or more bolts, pins, or " pegs " which will purposely *shear* (or " break off ") should the machine become overloaded. The coupling consists of two flanges, one of which is usually

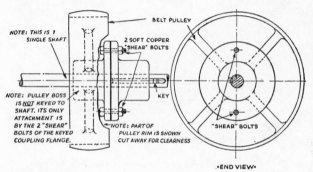

Fig. 83.—Shear-bolt Coupling (Adapted to a Belt-pulley).

attached to the boss of a pulley or gear-wheel, and the other is keyed to the shaft.

A typical example of application is shown in Fig. 83. In this case the pulley-boss is extended to form a flange, and the other flange, or half-coupling, is keyed to the shaft. The flanges are connected by means of two soft copper " shear-bolts," the size or cross-sectional area of which are pre-determined so as to be sufficiently strong to take the normal working load of the machine attached to the shaft. Should that load be exceeded, the bolts will " shear ", but the belt pulley, which may be driven from an engine, could continue to rotate idly on the shaft, and the machine would thus be protected from serious damage. After a " stoppage " in the machine has been accounted for, new " shear-bolts " would be fitted to the coupling and the machine re-started. This principle is often applied to crushing and grinding machinery for grain and other similar products.

It should be noted that the pulley-boss is not keyed to the shaft, and its only connection to it is through the coupling flanges, the right-hand side boss of which is keyed to the shaft.

A shear-bolt coupling may be fitted to a flange extended from a gear-wheel, or fly-wheel, or a chain-sprocket wheel, in a similar manner to that shown in the illustration. It may also be used for connecting two shafts endways on, provided that bearings are positioned on either side of the coupling in order to support the shafts in the event of the coupling bolts " shearing ".

As an alternative to copper, wood pegs, or even rods of vulcanite can be used, but for the drives of all machines the required horse-power must be known. This having been calculated or ascertained, then the coupling-bolts or pegs can be designed to have just sufficient strength for the power involved. Such couplings are usually made of cast iron or steel.

Jaw Coupling (or Jaw Clutch) (Fig. 84)

Up to now the various couplings considered have been those used for connecting shafts the ends of which butt up to each other, and in order to rotate them as one complete unit. Cases, however, occur in which it is desirable for two shafts to be in one straight line with their ends adjacent, yet some of the shafts may be required to rotate only occasionally. This can be effected by using a " jaw-coupling "—sometimes called a " jaw-clutch "—as is shown in Fig. 84.

Such a coupling is formed of two flanged bosses, both of which have jaws projecting from their inner faces. Some types have three jaws, and others may have four-jaw formations on each flange. The jaws of one half-coupling unit fit into the spaces between the jaws of its mating half.

From the illustration it will be seen that the half-coupling shown on the left side has an extended boss, which is recessed to accommodate the " fork " of an operating lever. By means of this the unit can be slid or moved along the shaft so as to engage with the jaws of the other half-coupling. The sliding movement is controlled by a forked operating lever, as shown in Fig. 84a. A " feather-key " is fitted to the shaft, which forms a guide for this movement, and the boss is a " working-fit " on the shaft and key.

The other half-coupling (shown to the right of the illustration) is securely keyed to its shaft in a *fixed* position. The

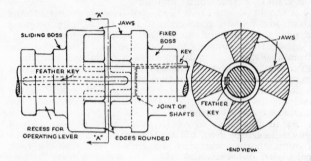

Fig. 84.—" Jaw " Coupling (Showing Jaws Disengaged).

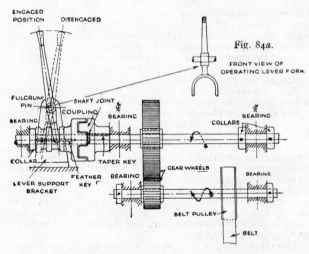

Fig. 85.—Application of " Jaw " Coupling.

two shafts can thus be coupled together or uncoupled as desired by operating the forked lever to engage or disengage the jaws.

This type of coupling is used for the above purpose on slow-speed shafts and those of large diameter, and it is used extensively on heavy classes of industrial machinery. The coupling is usually made of stout form in cast iron or cast steel, but for some classes of work it may be made of forged steel.

A typical example of its application is illustrated in Fig. 85, which shows how the *sliding-jaw* half-coupling may be mounted on a shaft which is constantly rotating. By movement of the forked lever, the jaws can be meshed with the other half-coupling—which is securely keyed to the large gear-wheel shaft—and thus bring the latter into motion, subsequently driving the smaller gear-wheel shaft.

This type of coupling can be used for a shaft which rotates slowly in either direction, for its jaws, being of flat formation, are enabled to engage irrespective of the direction in which its mating half-coupling might be rotating.

Claw Coupling (or Clutch) (Fig. 86)

A " claw " coupling is very similar to that just described, except that its teeth or jaws are claw-shaped or curved, as shown in the diagram. This type can be used for shafts where the speed of rotation is higher than that of the jaw type.

On account of the curved formation of its jaws or teeth, the claw type will engage more easily and the meshing process is of a more gradual character, which considerably facilitates the " engagement ", because the sliding unit, on being brought into contact with the fixed one during the latter's rotation, does not have to wait for the exact coincidence of the spaces between the jaws, but as soon as contact is made on any part of the claw's curved surface it is guided into mesh until complete engagement is attained.

The claw type coupling *cannot*, however, be used in either direction of rotation. It must rotate in the direction of the curve formation.

Referring to Fig. 86, the direction of rotation for that design of coupling is for the " fixed " unit to rotate in an anti-clockwise direction if it is attached to the *driving* shaft, as shown by the arrow in the end view " *BB* ".

Had the shaft been rotating in a clockwise direction, the curved formation of the claws would have been the opposite to those shown.

The principle will perhaps be understood better if reference is made to Figs. 86a and 86b. These illustrations show both the left-hand and right-hand types of claw couplings, with

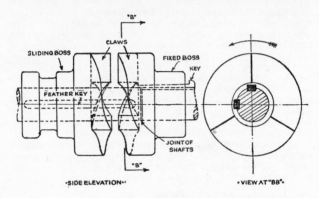

Fig. 86.—" Claw " Coupling (Disengaged).

a large arrow indicating the direction of rotation of the complete meshed coupling in each case, *but* when the *sliding-half* is attached to the *driving-shaft*. Should the fixed half-coupling be attached to the shaft which is driving, or

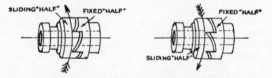

Fig. 86a.—Left-hand Type. Fig. 86b.—Right-hand Type.

rotating, however, then the direction of rotation would be the opposite to that indicated by the arrows.

The advantages of easier meshing and higher shaft speeds are somewhat offset by its limitation to rotate in one direction only.

Floating-centre Type Coupling (Fig. 87)

A " floating-centre " coupling of the kind shown in the illustration comprises three pieces only. These consist of two flanged half-coupling units, together with a common centre-piece. The flanged " halves "—which are made either of cast iron or steel—are grooved in order to accommodate the lugs which protrude from the centre-piece disc. The latter is made of solid steel, and the lugs or " tongues " which project from it are set at right angles to each other,

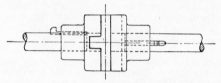

Fig. 87.—Floating-centre Type Coupling (assembled on shafts).

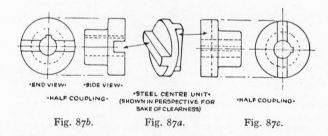

·END VIEW·   ·SIDE VIEW·

·HALF COUPLING·

·STEEL CENTRE UNIT·
(SHOWN IN PERSPECTIVE FOR
SAKE OF CLEARNESS)

·HALF COUPLING·

Fig. 87b.   Fig. 87a.   Fig. 87c.

thus preventing them from working out of the flange grooves during their rotation.

The lugs are consequently a sliding or working fit in the grooves of the flanges. That is to say, they are given a clearance fit to enable them to " float " or slide slightly. This therefore provides for slight axial movement of the shafts, and compensates for slight angular misalignment.

A coupling of this type is suitable for transmitting heavy loads applied to slow-speed shafts and those in which heavy torque is developed. The lugs are therefore of substantial formation, because they have to resist the torsional effect encountered. Each half-coupling is securely keyed to its respective shaft, as shown in the assembly view of Fig. 87. Figs. 87a, 87b, and 87c, show the individual parts before assembly. The steel centre-piece is shown in perspective view for clearness.

CLUTCHES

General

A " clutch " is a kind of coupling, by means of which two shafts may be connected or disconnected at will. It may also be formed of two parts, both of which are mounted on the same shaft, one part keyed to the shaft and the other mounted loosely on the shaft, but in such a manner that the two parts can be engaged and caused to rotate as one unit.

The " loose " part can be also " disengaged " at will, so as to come to rest, whilst the other (keyed part) continues to rotate on the shaft. This has a distinct advantage, because a pulley can be attached to the loose part of the clutch and caused to rotate when so desired in order to drive a machine intermittently.

In its general application, a clutch is very similar to the jaw- or claw-type couplings shown in Figs. 84, 85, 86 and 87. In fact, they are sometimes referred to as " clutches ", and for *low-speed* shafts may often be used as such.

Owing to the difficulty of engaging—or meshing—jaw- or claw-type units when attached to *high-speed* shafts, however, other types have to be used. These sometimes take the form of a steel disc, and a disc of cork, leather, fabric, or special asbestos bonded with brass wire, etc., in order to produce a surface which will grip the plain steel disc. The clutch-plates are usually retained firmly together (when engaged) by springs, which cause the two disc faces to be held together by friction only.

Another type of clutch is the " cone ". This employs a similar principle of gripping by the friction derived between the surfaces, but instead of the clutch being of flat disc formation, it consists of a hollow conical-shaped cylinder into which fits another, the outer surface of which is " faced " with some material which develops a frictional grip when pressure is exerted to force it into the outer cone.

Disc-type Friction Clutch (Fig. 88)

A " friction " clutch is one which relies on the friction between its faces in order to effect the grip. In order to assist the friction, springs are usually employed in one form or another which increase the pressure exerted between the faces of the " clutch-plate " and the friction member.

From the illustration of Fig. 88 it will be seen that there is a " plain " clutch-plate which forms the left-hand side member, and the right-hand side clutch-plate has a friction disc secured to it by countersunk rivets. It also has a long boss attached, to which the operating-lever fork fits, and it is consequently provided with a means of sliding along the shaft. It is retained in position by a feather key.

The coil-type spring is positioned around the shaft, and bears on to the shoulder of the clutch-plate boss, which acts as a collar. The spring is held in position by another collar.

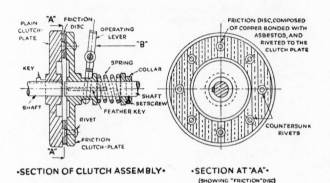

•SECTION OF CLUTCH ASSEMBLY•   •SECTION AT "AA"•
(SHOWING "FRICTION"DISC)

Fig. 88.

The latter can be slid along the shaft and set-screwed in position so as to give the required amount of compression to the spring which exerts pressure on to the friction clutch-plate. This pressure causes an efficient grip to be made when the plates engage one another, and unites them as one member when being driven. When it is desired to disengage the clutch, this is effected by pushing the operating lever—in the direction of arrow " B " (shown in the illustration). By so doing, the spring is compressed more, thus permitting the friction-plate boss to slide along the shaft, and the contact between the faces of the two clutch-plates is broken or separated.

The clutch shown in Fig. 88 is of elementary pattern, and

is often used for industrial machinery. After prolonged use, when the friction-disc becomes badly worn down so as to expose the countersunk heads of the rivets, it can be unriveted and a new disc fitted. The clutch-plates are usually made of either cast iron or steel, and the inner faces are accurately machined in order to assure even and smooth surfaces.

This type of clutch when used on motor-cars is usually modified by the use of several springs in place of one central spring. These are evenly spaced around positions adjacent to the friction-disc, in order to give more even pressure.

Cone-type Friction Clutch (Fig. 89)

Instead of having plain flat discs as friction members, this has one of " conical " shape. The fly-wheel (or gear-wheel)

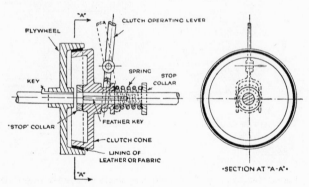

Fig. 89.—Friction Clutch (Cone Type).

with which the clutch operates has its rim " inner-face " machined to a similar cone slope, and its boss is securely keyed to the shaft on which it is mounted.

The clutch " cone " has its outer " rim-face " fitted with leather, fabric, or asbestos and fabric combined, so as to form the friction element, and this is secured by countersunk copper rivets.

Extending from the main boss of the clutch-cone is a

" recessed boss ", into which fits the fork of the operating lever, as shown in the illustration. The clutch-cone boss is mounted as a sliding fit on its respective shaft, and is located in position by a feather key, along which it is also free to slide, and at the end of the shaft a " collar " is fitted which acts as a " stop ".

At the other end of the boss a coil-type spring is mounted around the shaft. The spring is of sufficient internal diameter to clear the feather key, and is located in position in shallow recesses of the collar formed on the extended boss, also of the collar which secures the spring in position along the shaft.

On reference being made to the illustration (Fig. 89) it will be seen that the clutch is in the engaged position and the operating lever is shown in " full " outline. The dotted outline shows the position of the operating lever when the clutch cone is disengaged. In the latter position the spring is compressed, or its coils are closed up, and the collar on the shaft retains the spring in position.

It will be realised from the foregoing remarks that by this means the clutch may be used for connecting together two shafts, when one of these is required to be rotated only occasionally.

When the clutch is engaged, the friction cone is held in position entirely by the force exerted by the spring, but when it is disengaged the lever must be retained in the position shown by dotted lines in order to keep the spring compressed. This is usually achieved by fitting a " quadrant " of either the " ratchet " type, or one with a hole and a " peg " at some convenient position along the lever.

As wear takes place on the cone lining it penetrates farther into the fly-wheel rim, and when a considerable amount of wear has taken place the lining can be renewed. The " stop " collars are set-screwed to the shaft so that their positions can be adjusted to suit.

Both the fly-wheel and clutch-cone are usually made of cast iron. The forked operating lever is made of mild steel, and is of similar construction to that shown in Fig. 84a.

Cylindrical-friction Clutch or Internal-expanding Shoe Type (Fig. 90)

A common clutch used extensively for heavy industrial machinery is the " cylindrical-friction " type. On reference being made to Fig. 90, this may appear complicated at first sight, but if studied closely it should not be found difficult to understand the principle on which it operates. If compared with the clutches previously dealt with, this type certainly does consist of many more parts.

It comprises an " outer shell " in the form of a " wheel " which has a flange on one side only. Its boss is fitted with a gun-metal bush, because, instead of it being keyed to the shaft, it is free to rotate. On account of this, and in order to resist wear, a lubricator must be provided. The wheel-boss is retained in position on the shaft by a loose collar fitted with one or more set-screws.

The inner face of the " clutch-shell " is accurately

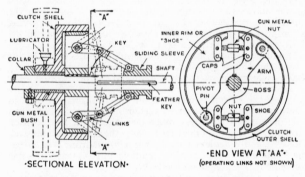

Fig. 90.—Internal-expanding Shoe Type Clutch.

machined, and inside the shell is fitted another " wheel ", but in the form of a boss which is keyed to the shaft and from which project two " arms ". Mounted on these arms are two semi-circular shaped " shoes " which form an inner " rim ". These are pivoted to the arms as shown in the end view of Fig. 90.

At the positions shown are two square gun-metal nuts, mounted on spindles. By manipulation of the nuts the " shoes " are expanded by the left- and right-hand screws, which are retained in position by the caps. The operation of the nuts is effected from the " links " that are attached to a " sliding sleeve " mounted on the shaft, as shown in the sectional elevation of Fig. 90. The sleeve and links are shown in full lines representing the disengaged position of the clutch, and the dotted lines show the engaged position when the nuts have thus been turned by sliding the sleeve along the shaft and subsequently operating the links.

The sliding sleeve is operated by means of a forked lever, similar to that used for jaw and claw couplings, and as illustrated in Fig. 84a.

The clutch " shell " and " shoes " are usually made of cast iron, and the friction surfaces are accurately machined. The shoes, in some cases, may have friction linings fitted to their outer faces which increase their efficiency.

A belt-pulley is often used in conjunction with this type of clutch for driving a machine intermittently, and the belt pulley-boss is keyed to the boss of the clutch-shell. Such a pulley is shown in dotted outline in the sectional elevation of Fig. 90.

When a pulley is attached to the clutch-shell in this manner, it may be stationary whilst the shaft is rotating, and the clutch must be engaged to bring the pulley into use.

On the other hand, the pulley may be driven from an engine or electric motor by means of a belt, and the shaft may be stationary and coupled to a machine. By engaging the clutch, therefore, the machine can be brought into operation.

The clutch requires careful and accurate assembling, as it relies entirely on the pressure exerted by the shoes to obtain its grip, which requires the operating lever to be retained constantly so as to " thrust " the sleeve towards the boss of the inner rim. It will be noticed that with this type of clutch no springs are employed.

The clutch can also be used for bringing into motion a second shaft positioned parallel to the first, as shown in Fig. 85.

Furthermore, instead of having a pulley attached to the shell, a gear-wheel could be fixed to it, and used for operating the second shaft of Fig. 85. In such a case the clutch would be positioned to the right-hand side of the large gear-wheel, thus dispensing with the jaw coupling shown in the left-hand view of the illustration.

Automatic Centrifugal Clutch (Fig. 90a)

This is another interesting type and is automatic in its action. When the electric motor—to which it is attached—has attained a certain speed the centrifugal force of the

" trip levers " overcomes the pressure of the " springs " which open outwards, releasing the " shoes ". These move outwards and press against the inner surface of the rim.   The

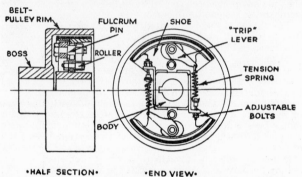

•HALF SECTION•   •END VIEW•

Fig. 90a.—Automatic Centrifugal Clutch

Reproduced by permission of Frank Wigglesworth and Co., Ltd.

full load of the " drive " is consequently picked up gradually and automatically.

CHAPTER VII

BEARINGS (GENERAL)

(Plain, Bushed, Split-step, Ball, Roller, and Special Types)

CONSIDERATION may now be given to the components in which shafts are supported, or " mounted ", in order that they

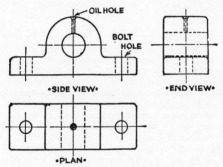

Fig. 91.—Cast Iron " Filbow " or Eye-bearing.

may rotate freely. Such components are called " bearings ", " journals ", " pedestals ", or " plummer-blocks ", etc. There are many types of bearings, varying from plain cast iron to those of the " ball " or " roller-race " pattern. Naturally, each kind has its specific purpose. One type of bearing might be quite suitable for a slow-speed shaft, yet totally unsuitable for shafts of high-speed rotation. It is therefore proposed to consider each type in order of this chapter heading.

PLAIN-TYPE BEARING (Fig. 91)

A plain bearing of only small size is called a " filbow " " dead eye ", or " eye-bearing ". These terms apply to components with " bore " diameters up to approximately 50·800 mm. (2 inches).

Note.—Above this size they are usually called plain bearings. Such components are used for supporting light spindles, or shafts of small diameter only.

A " filbow " consists of a flat base, from which projects a boss of semi-circular shape, as shown in the illustration.

The base has a bolt-hole positioned near each end for bolting it in position, and the boss is bored or drilled to suit the diameter of the spindle or shaft concerned. Through the boss is drilled a small oil-hole, in order to lubricate the shaft.

Filbows or " eye-bearings " are mostly made of cast iron, and the distance through the boss is usually equal to one and a half times or twice that of the shaft diameter concerned, and the thickness of the metal is relatively proportionate.

GUN-METAL BUSHED EYE-BEARING (Fig. 92)

For work of more importance, or for a small-diameter shaft rotating at a higher speed, a type similar to that shown in Fig. 92 would probably be used. From the illustration it will be seen that this bearing has a brass or gun-metal bush fitted to its bore. It is of plain cylindrical shape, and is a tight driven fit into the bore.

In order to secure it in position and to prevent it from rotating, a " snug " is screwed into a " tapped " hole at the position indicated. A " snug " is a set-screw which, after having been tightly screwed into the bearing, has its head sawn off. As an alternative to using a set-screw, a plain round pin is sometimes driven in tightly, and its projecting end cut off.

It will be noticed that there are small bosses at the bolt-hole positions and that the bolt-holes are of " slotted " formation. This is to allow some latitude for lining up the shaft truly, for the eye-bearing can be moved lengthways in order to compensate for misalignment of the shaft or spindle.

When using this class of bearing a hard-wood packing is sometimes placed below the flat base to act as a cushion and to assist with the shaft alignment. The wood packing can be planed down to the exact thickness required.

Instead of the bearing having a totally flat surface to its base, a recess is formed centrally, as shown by dotted lines in the illustration, and only the outer edges rest on the wood packing. Should the base be slightly irregular, it is only necessary to " chip " and " file " the edges of the base, instead of the whole width, in order to obtain a good fit. The recess does not extend to the bolt-hole positions, as there must be all solid metal immediately between the bolt head and the nut, so that when the latter is tightened there is no bending tendency created on the base.

Brass bushed bearings of the above type are often used for shafts up to 76·200 mm. (3 inches) or so in diameter, and may be used for even larger diameters of slow-speed shafts.

The advantage of using brass or gun-metal for bearing " bushes " is that it wears better than plain cast iron, also after prolonged use the " bushes " can be renewed, whereas

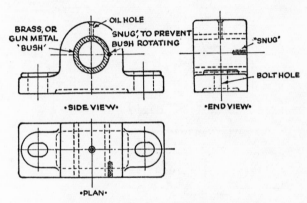

•SIDE VIEW•　　•END VIEW•

•PLAN•

Fig. 92.—Gun-metal Bushed Eye-bearing.

when plain cast-iron bearings become badly worn they are either " scrapped " or, provided there is sufficient metal thickness, bored out and fitted with bushes.

In order to fit a shaft into this type of bearing it is, of course necessary to insert it endwise. This can easily be effected when light spindles or small shafts are dealt with, but it becomes more difficult with shafts of larger size, especially if the latter have large gear-wheels or pulleys fitted to them.

" SPLIT-STEP " TYPE BEARING OR " PEDESTAL "
(Fig. 93)

A " pedestal "—sometimes called a " plummer-block " or " pillow-block "—is a form of bearing whose " steps " or brasses are formed of two " halves ". These are usually referred to as *top* " *brass* " and *bottom* " *brass* ". The brasses are fitted into the pedestal body, which is made of cast iron and secured by a cap held by bolts, as shown in the illustration.

The length of the brasses (or " steps ") may be one and a half, two, or even three times the size of the diameter of the shaft, according to the duty or nature of the work they have to perform.

The brasses, being of cylindrical formation, are liable to rotate with the shaft. In order to prevent such rotation,

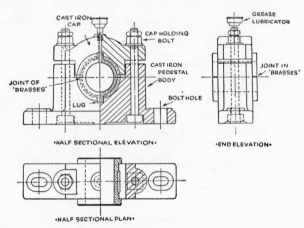

Fig. 93.—Typical " Pedestal " or Plummer-block
(Upright Type).

various means are employed, one of which is to incorporate a lug in each " half brass ", which fits into recesses formed in the pedestal body and the cap, as shown in Fig. 93*a*. Another method is to make the brass body of octagonal formation, as shown in Fig. 93*b*. The faces of these formations are then " bedded " on to similar formations of the pedestal body and its cap. It is also possible to make the brass body of square formation, with its centre bored out circular. The square faces then fit into similar-shaped recesses of the body and cap.

The " joint " of the two brasses is horizontal or parallel

to the length of the shaft. As wear takes place on the brass inner surfaces with which the shaft forms contact, the pedestal can be dismantled and the joint faces filed down to compensate for the wear, and the cap-bolts can then be tightened correspondingly. It will be seen in the assembly illustration of Fig. 93 that there is a clearance provided between the cap and the pedestal-body for this purpose.

When a pedestal is fitted to a machine, its cap and top brass can be removed, the shaft inserted, so as to " bed down " or sit on the lower brass; then the top-brass, together with pedestal cap, can be replaced and the bolts finally tightened.

In order to provide means of lubrication, the top-brass

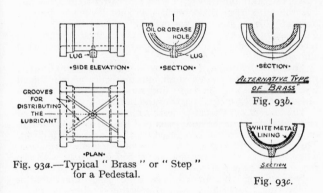

Fig. 93a.—Typical " Brass " or " Step "
for a Pedestal.

ALTERNATIVE TYPE
OF " BRASS "
Fig. 93b.

Fig. 93c.

is drilled at the lug position, and is then fitted with a grease-cup or oil-type lubricator. In order to distribute the lubricant from the central feed point over the whole surface of the brass, grooves or channels are cut in the latter, as shown in the plan view of Fig. 93a.

A pedestal of this type usually has a wood strip fitted between its base and the part of the machine on which it rests, in order to form a cushion. The wood strip can be shaved or planed down in order to allow for true alignment of the shaft, and the pedestal base-bolt holes are of slotted formation in order to provide for sideways alignment.

The brasses or " steps " for such pedestals are made of gun-metal or phosphor-bronze, both of which are of a somewhat similar colour to that of " brass ", from which the term

" *brasses* " possibly originated. Both gun-metal and phosphor-bronze are hard and durable, and stand up well to prolonged use.

In view of this hardness, and also that of the shafts which they carry, it is essential to ensure that as perfect alignment as possible is obtained when mounting the shafts. Unless close attention is paid to this process " binding " will be created in odd places, instead of the shaft surface lying equally and evenly over the whole area of the brass.

In some instances an " anti-friction " alloy—known as " white metal " or Babbitt's metal—is used as a lining for the brasses. This alloy considerably reduces the friction between the shaft and the step. It is also softer than brass, and has the advantage that the fit need not be made quite so accurate (as a step of gun-metal) to the relative shaft. Furthermore, it can be " run " when in a molten state into recesses of the step to form a lining, as shown in the section of Fig. 93c.

Another advantage of white metal is that, being of a softer nature than gun-metal, a shaft automatically " beds " itself into the metal and tends to find its own alignment, which obviates binding on any parts of the bearing.

The brasses or steps of pedestals must be accurately fitted or bedded down to the body-part and the cap of the pedestal, or undue pressure will be caused on the places which do fit. This particularly applies to brasses of octagonal formation, when all sides of the octagon must bed efficiently with the recess faces of the pedestal.

Pedestals or " plummer blocks " are used extensively in engineering, especially for supporting " line-shafting ", because a shaft complete with its pulleys, gear-wheels, collars, couplings, etc., can be easily mounted in them by merely removing the pedestal cap and top brass, which is a distinct advantage over the one-piece " bush " type of bearing. Furthermore, new brasses can easily be fitted when required.

For pedestals of large size four bolt-holes are provided in the base instead of two as shown in the illustration. The number of bolt-holes is often governed by the member on which the pedestal has to be bolted, for if it has to be accommodated on a rolled-steel " channel " or angle iron, only two bolt-holes are necessary, but should the support member be a " rolled-steel joist " or " I " beam, it is then necessary to have four bolt-holes, in order to have two bolts each side of the joist " web " or central part.

The pedestal shown in Fig. 93 is known as an " upright " type. It will be appreciated that when a shaft is normally mounted in a pedestal, the shaft-load is transmitted to the lower brass. If the shaft carries a pulley which is driven from an engine or electric motor situated on the ground below, the pull developed from the belt-drive increases the load, in addition to that derived from the weights of the shaft, pulley and collars, etc.

If the motor be mounted in such a position, however, that the belt-pull is in a horizontal direction, instead of upright pedestals, a type known as " angular " pedestals would no doubt be used, especially if the belt-pull is great.

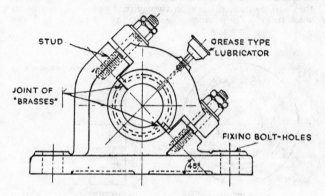

Fig. 94.—Angular Type Pedestal.

ANGULAR PEDESTAL (Fig. 94)

The joint formation of an angular pedestal is set at an angle relative to its base. Such a pedestal is shown in side elevation of Fig. 94. From this it will be seen that the joints of the brasses are at an angle of 45° from the base of the pedestal body, and the cap is also set at a similar incline.

The force exerted by a shaft, together with any gearing or pulleys mounted on it, is in a downward vertical direction, but should the belt-drive of the shaft be of a horizontal nature, the resulting force direction would probably be in the region of 45°, so the direction of pressure on the lower brass would also be at that angle, and an angular pedestal would be used.

In addition to angular pedestals of 45°, different inclinations are sometimes used. A common type is one of 30°.

It is sometimes difficult to use bolts for securing the caps of angular pedestals, and studs are frequently used for this purpose. Some types have a bolt for the top cap end connection and a stud for the lower one.

BALL-TYPE BEARING (Fig. 95)

A " ball-bearing " is one which makes use of hardened steel " balls " instead of plain cast-iron, gun-metal, etc., for its bearing surfaces. Instead of the rolling elements (steel balls) forming direct contact with the shaft concerned, they are positioned between two suitably grooved, hardened steel rings. These rings are known as " races ", and the

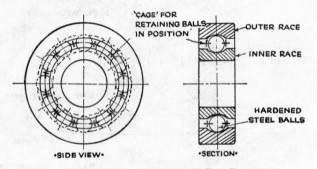

Fig. 95.—Ball-bearing (Single Row Type).

rolling elements are retained in position by a separator or " cage "—usually of pressed or drilled brass, bronze aluminium, or " Bakelite " (trade term) construction—thereby maintaining each " ball " in its allotted position. The " inner race " should be a " drive fit " on the shaft, so as to rotate with it. The " outer race " should not rotate, but should fit tightly into a " housing " of similar construction to a light-type pedestal body.

The theory involved in a ball-bearing is that, owing to the balls being spherical, " point contact " only is made between them and the tracks, thereby eliminating a large surface area of contact. As the balls are free to rotate, only " rolling friction " is caused, which is very small compared with the

" sliding friction " encountered with plain-bushed bearings—where whole surfaces are in direct contact with the shaft, thus providing large friction areas.

Theoretically, a ball-bearing requires no lubrication—since point-contact only is involved. Practically, however, owing to the shape of the balls and their tracks, the contact area is elliptical, so, to lubricate this area and the " rubbing " surface between the balls and cage, good-quality mineral oil or grease lubrication must be provided.

In addition, the lubricant affords protection from corrosion due to moisture or harmful gases in the atmosphere.

The steel employed for the manufacture of the rolling elements is capable of being heat-treated so as to attain a very high degree of hardness. This, coupled with the highly polished surfaces provided, also the small areas of contact between them and their races, together with the rolling action, reduces friction to an absolute minimum.

These rolling elements are manufactured to a very high degree of accuracy—to a ten-thousandth part of an inch, or even finer limits—both for diameter and sphericity (roundness).

At both ends of the housing through which the shaft passes oiled felt rings (washers) are frequently fitted in order to prevent grit penetrating into the races.

For higher speeds, however, various types of labyrinth are used to provide the protection from foreign matter.

Incidentally, prior to despatch from the manufacturers' works the complete ball races are dipped in grease or rust-proofing oil, after which they are usually wrapped in grease-proof paper, which should preferably not be removed until they are to be assembled in their housings for service—thereby preventing the ingress of grit or dirt.

Many forms of ball-bearings are used in engineering; that illustrated in Fig. 95 is known as a " single-row " type, and is used extensively for high-speed shafts carrying light or medium loads.

Double-row Ball-bearing (Self-aligning Type) (Fig. 96)

This type has two rows of steel balls in its cage. The two rows are " staggered "—*i.e.* any ball of one row is so positioned that it is diagonally in between two balls of the adjacent row, instead of being precisely side by side. It will be seen from the illustration, therefore, that the balls in one row do not touch those in the other. It will also be observed that the rolling elements are positioned axially away from the centre of the whole bearing. The outer surface of the inner race is grooved to give an individual track for each row of balls; the inner surface of the outer race is of spherical formation, thereby providing one common track for both rows of steel balls.

This design of bearing allows it to compensate for any misalignment between shaft and housing, since the inner race, together with its complement of balls, can align itself freely about the bearing centre.

Further, by this means the outer race can be applied to the cage—during assembly—by tilting or swivelling it about the

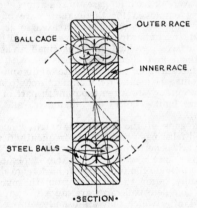

Fig. 96.—Ball-bearing (Double Row Radial, or Self-aligning Type).

[Reproduced by permission of Messrs. The Hoffmann Manufacturing Co., Ltd.

centre axis of the whole bearing, thereby facilitating its fitting.

The load-carrying capacity of this " self-aligning " type of bearing, however, is not quite so high as that of the single-row pattern, because, despite the greater number of steel balls, the degree of conformity between the balls and outer race track is not so high. With this self-aligning type " rolling " friction only is concerned, as in the case of the single-row pattern depicted in Fig. 95.

Many other types of ball-bearing are used in engineering, some of which are designed specially to carry " end-thrust ".

Ball-bearings are very compact, and take up less space in

length than gun-metal bushed, ring-oiled, or plain pedestal types. They are efficient in use, require very little attention, and can be used for shafts at very high speeds of rotation.

It is essential, however, for ball-races to be correctly assembled and carefully fitted in their housings in order to obtain efficient service from them.

Roller-bearing (Elementary Type) (Fig. 97)

A "roller-bearing" is one fitted with a series of rollers (small hardened steel cylinders) instead of steel balls, in order to form its rolling elements.

The chief difference between ball- and roller-bearings is that in the case of the former there is theoretical point-contact between the balls and their tracks, whereas in the case of a

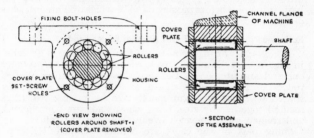

Fig. 97.—Roller-bearing (Elementary Type).

roller-bearing the rollers form "line-contact" with their tracks—*i.e.* the rollers bear on the tracks for the whole of their length, which means an increase in the load-carrying capacity of the bearing : a distinct advantage where the shaft loads are heavy.

It will be appreciated that in the case of the ball-bearing previously considered the load transmitted from the shaft tends to *crush* the balls and *indent* the track. This tendency is resisted by the high class of steel used and the degree of hardness attained in their manufacture.

It will also be realised that the points of contact between the balls and their tracks are very small, but when rollers are used these point contacts extend for the whole length of the rollers, thereby providing a considerably larger surface of support to resist the crushing effect of the load.

The bearing illustrated in Fig. 97 is an elementary one, in

which plain hardened-steel rollers are placed around the shaft, and are held in position by the housing end-pieces. The latter is of the eye-bearing pattern, and is made of cast iron. Its bore is accurately and smoothly machined to allow the rollers to rotate freely. An oil-hole is usually drilled in any convenient position through the housing flange to provide for lubrication of the rollers.

A bearing of the foregoing description is used frequently for cheap classes of work, such as trolleys or trucks for industrial work. Trucks fitted with such bearings require far less manual effort for pushing around a factory than those fitted with plain cast iron " filbows " or gun-metal bushed bearings. Although this type of roller bearing is of rather crude design, it is hoped that a useful purpose is served by introducing it to the reader in order to acquaint him with the basic principles before passing on to bearings of more intricate design.

Roller-bearing (Precision Type) (Parallel Roller Kind)

A high-class or precision-type of roller-bearing is depicted in Fig. 98. It comprises two hardened steel races : an inner one and an outer one. Between these races hardened steel rollers are positioned as shown, and are retained in equally spaced positions by a gun-metal cage comprising two rings secured together by steel pins, whose ends are countersunk and riveted over. Spaced evenly between the rollers, and forming part of the cage, are suitably shaped " distant-pieces ", which thus provide " working clearances " for the rollers. The rollers and races are accurately " ground " to a fine finish—" standards " similar to those described for ball-bearings being worked to by the manufacturers.

The inner race of this bearing is a " drive-fit " on to the shaft concerned, and rotates with it. The outer-race (like that of the ball-type) is firmly secured in a housing, and does *not* rotate, but the rollers are free to rotate, and do so. A shaft mounted in a roller-bearing of this type requires very little power to rotate it.

This class of bearing having rollers (whose entire lengths form " bearing contact " with the races) provides greater capacity than a ball-type bearing for carrying heavy shaft-loads, or, alternatively, a smaller bearing of roller-type might be used for a corresponding shaft-load. The most common kind employed is one having rollers equal in diameter to their length, but in some cases longer rollers are used.

Usually the outer surface of the inner race is grooved to form the running-track for the rollers.

Outer races may be formed with or without internal grooves, depending on the design and the respective use.

This type of bearing is employed extensively in high-class machinery, and can be used for high speeds combined with heavy loads.

The shaft concerned must, however, be fed through the bore of the bearing to fix it in position, but must *not* be fitted too tightly, or undue stresses are likely to be set up in the race, thereby resulting in a possible breakdown.   As no pro-

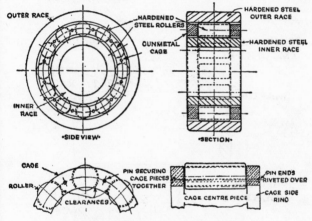

Fig. 98.—Roller-bearing (Precision Type).
Enlarged Views of Sections.

vision can be made for misalignment, it is very essential that the shaft should be truly " lined-up ".

For this class of bearing similar lubrication should be provided to that supplied for ball-bearings.

In addition to the use of the foregoing parallel-type of roller, sometimes those of " tapered " formation are employed complete with suitably tapered races.

These can be used for normal bearing loads, combined with those of end-thrust.

Other types of roller-bearings cater for shaft misalignment, by their being mounted in swivel-type housings, thus permitting the complete bearing to swivel in its supports.

Split Type Roller-bearing in Spherical Mounting (Fig. 99)

A further type of roller-bearing is that shown in the illustration mounted in a " spherical " housing. From the diagram (Fig. 99) it will be seen that the " outer " surface of the " outer " race is curved, or is of " spherical " shape to suit the housing or pedestal in which it is retained.

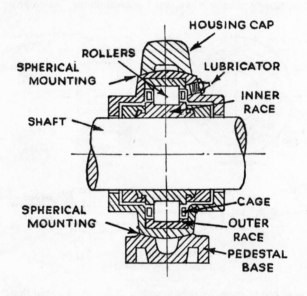

Fig. 99.—Split Type Roller-bearing (in spherical mounting)

Reproduced by permission of
Cooper Roller Bearings Co., Ltd.

With this arrangement the complete roller-bearing is free to move axially in the pedestal housing. This provision caters for any slight " misalignment " of the shaft; for the bearing automatically finds its own true " line-up " to suit the shaft. Such a bearing is known as a " self-aligning " type.

This type of bearing is of the " split " pattern. That is

to say, its inner and outer races, also the cage, are all made in halves, which are bolted together as shown (see Fig. 99a).

Some designs have the " race " made in two halves, each of which is " stepped ", or recessed and held together by set-screws instead of having bosses and clamping bolts to secure them.

All such designs are a great advantage, for the bearing can be dismantled easily and the shaft inserted in a similar

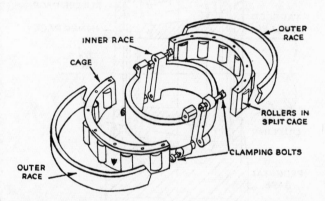

Fig. 99a.—Sketch Showing Typical Details of Split Roller Cage and Race, etc.

manner to that of an ordinary " split-type " gun-metal bushed pedestal previously described.

Bearings of this type will often give as much as twenty years efficient service, when used on general engineering or industrial machinery.

Tapered Roller-bearing (Fig. 100)

These have rollers of slightly tapered formation held in position in a specially shaped cage. If necessary, wear can thus be taken up, or provided for in this design. Such bearings, in addition to being used for high class general engineering work, are also widely used in the motor-car industry.

E

From the illustration it will be seen that both the inner and outer races are of special shape in order to accommodate and retain the rollers in their relative positions.

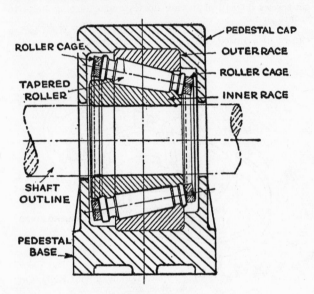

Fig. 100.—Tapered Roller-bearing.

Needle Roller-bearing

This type might be considered as resembling a parallel-roller bearing in general principle, but having very small rollers (or " needles ") of 2 mms. to 10 mms. diameter for its rolling elements.

The lengths of the needles are frequently between five and ten times their diameter. Their end formations may be of convex semicircular formation, or of rounded conical shape.

The needles are mounted between two hardened steel races, but no cage is used. The inner race is usually of plain hollow cylindrical form, but the outer one is recessed to accommodate hardened end-pieces, which retain the needles in position.

Such bearings occupy very little overall space for diameter, and are very compact. They are used extensively on aircraft for bearings carrying controls, etc., or for light loads in confined spaces. Their component parts are made to the same " standards " of accuracy as those described earlier for ball- and roller-bearings, and similar forms of lubrication are used.

HYATT-WOUND ROLLER-TYPE BEARING

A further bearing is the " Hyatt "-wound roller-type. It is widely used and has some interesting features. This bearing is composed of rollers of helical formation, made from wound strips of alloy steel.

The rollers are suitably heat-treated, thereby attaining the required toughness and hardness, and ground to precision limits. They are held in proper alignment by means of a cage consisting of two pressed-steel end-rings, rigidly secured by round steel spacing-bars, the ends of which are riveted into the end-rings.

The rollers are wound alternately right and left hand, so that lubricant is swept to and fro across the operating surfaces.

These roller assemblies are frequently used with rolled-steel outer races, or solid inner and outer races, and may be mounted in rigid pedestals or self-aligning plummer blocks and axle-boxes, loose pulleys, truck wheels, etc.

For line-shafting purposes these bearings and shafting boxes are supplied split in halves, to facilitate erection and dismantling without removal of pulley and couplings, etc.

Numerous other types of Hyatt roller-bearings are also available, but space does not permit further details.

SUMMARY

For all classes of ball- and roller-bearings close attention should be paid to their fitting to the shafts and housings.

This especially applies to the " non-self-aligning " types, in which case every precaution must be taken to see that the shaft and housing are " lined up " as truly as possible.

The inner race should not be too tight or too loose on the shaft, and should rotate with it, the actual " fit " being dependent on the loads applied.

Oiled felt (or other types of washers) is frequently fitted in the housing on both sides of the bearing to form " seals " and prevent dirt or grit from entering.

The chief claim for these classes of bearings is that friction is reduced to a minimum, as compared with bearings of plain-bush types. As an example, compare the moving of one piece of heavy furniture—having plain legs—over a floor, with that of another of similar weight, but having legs fitted with castors, rollers, or small wheels. The effort required to move the former—in which " sliding "-friction is concerned—is far greater than in the latter, involving only " rolling "-friction.

Note.—The terms " sliding " and " rolling " friction are used merely as illustrations, in the hope that they will be better understood by the reader.

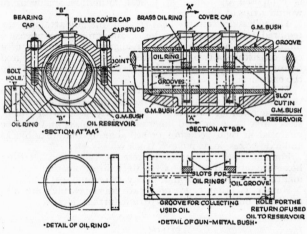

Fig. 101*b*.

Fig. 101.—Ring-oiled Bearing (Two-ring Type).

RING-OILED BEARING (Fig. 101)

Of special interest is the ring-oiled bearing. This is un-doubtedly more efficient than those having plain gunmetal bushes, when used for relative high speeds, and it is also less expensive to produce than those of the ball or roller pattern. It consists of a gun-metal bush which has one or more slots cut out of the top, as shown in Fig. 101*b*. At the slot posi-tions plain brass rings of larger diameter are placed, which rest or float on the top of the shaft, and are free to rotate with it, as shown in Fig. 101. Being of larger diameter than the bush, the lower parts of the rings are positioned in the oil reservoir of the bearing, which is kept full of oil. Consequently, as the rings rotate with the shaft, oil is picked up and carried to the top of the shaft, where it is distributed along the length of the shaft inside the bearing by longitudinal grooves or " oil channels " inside the bush. At both ends of the bush circular grooves are formed in which the oil collects, and at the base of these grooves holes are drilled, through which the " used " oil is returned to the reservoir. Therefore, by means of the brass oil rings the oil is constantly re-circulated during the rotation of the shaft.

At a convenient position in the base of the reservoir a drain-plug is placed. This provides for the oil being drawn off—after prolonged use—and fresh oil applied by means of the filler at the top of the bearing-cap.

Sometimes, instead of being flat, these oil-rings are formed of triangular section with the peak of the triangle at the outside. It is claimed that such a formation distributes the oil better than the flat type.

The bush should be held in the bearing-base by a " snug " or set-screw, in order to prevent it from inadvertently rotating with the shaft should it for any reason work loose, as it is essential that the bush should remain in position with the slots for the rings in their correct uppermost position.

Bearings of the " ring-oiled " type are made with one, two, or four rings, depending on the nature of the work for which they are required. For some classes of jobs the bush may be lined with white metal (Babbitt metal) in a similar manner to those of ordinary pedestals or bearings.

One of the advantages of the ring-oiled bearing is that it can be used for considerable periods without attention, as the oil in the reservoir is used over and over again. Precautions should be taken, however, to see that the oil level in the reservoir never gets below that of the ring-base.

Some designs of ring-oiled bearings, instead of being fitted with circular oil-collecting grooves at the ends of the bushes, are left plain, and the pedestal base is extended beyond the end of the bush. Oil-collecting grooves are then formed in this base, by means of which the used oil flows towards the centre of the reservoir, where it is collected for further use.

CHAPTER VIII

GEARING—SPUR, BEVEL, MITRE, WORM, BELT, CHAIN, COTTON-ROPE AND "VEE"-ROPE TYPES, ETC. (GENERAL)

GEARING is the term generally applied to a series of two or more toothed wheels which are " meshed " together to form a "drive". It is also applied to "sprocket"-toothed wheels on which chains are mounted, and to two or more pulleys on which a belt is mounted to form a drive.

A " train " of gears is the name used for a number of toothed wheels in mesh with each other.

Let us now consider in detail the various types in order of the above heading.

SPUR-GEARS (Figs. 102 and 103)

One of the most common forms of gears is perhaps the " spur " type. This is a wheel which has teeth of a certain formation that mesh or fit into the spaces between the teeth of another similar wheel. If the latter is of smaller diameter than the former it is then known as a " pinion ".

A pinion is usually of solid block construction, whereas a gear-wheel is composed of a boss from which arms project and carry the rim of the wheel on which the teeth are formed. In order to understand gears thoroughly, there are several principles and further "terms" with which the student should acquaint himself (see Fig. 102).

The " pitch " of gear-wheel teeth may be stated in two forms:

[*Note*.—The reader is referred to I.S.O. recommendation R.54 (Modules and Diametrical Pitches of Cylindrical Gears) pending the publication of the relevant British Std. Specification.]

(1) The " circular pitch " is the distance from centre to centre of the teeth when measured along the " pitch circle ".

(2) The " diametral pitch " is the number of teeth per inch of diameter of the pitch circle, which is in reality a ratio of " Pi " (π). Therefore a gear wheel with teeth having a " circular pitch " of 79·771 mm.

(3·1416 inches) would be said to have a " diametral pitch " of No. 1.

Similarly, the teeth of a gear-wheel with a "circular pitch" of 39·900 mm. (1·5708 inches) would have "diametral pitch" No. 2, and so on.

Both terms are used extensively in engineering, so it is important to specify distinctly which pitch is intended, or referred to, when speaking of gears. If one type of pitch is given, the other type can be ascertained from the following formulæ:—

$$\text{CIRCULAR PITCH} \quad \frac{3·1416}{\text{The Diametral Pitch}} \qquad \text{DIAMETRAL PITCH} \quad \frac{3·1416}{\text{The Circular Pitch}}$$

Spur-gears are often "cast" (or made by moulding them to shape), in which case the teeth are left in a fairly rough state.

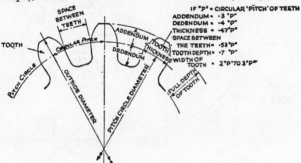

Fig. 102.—Details and Terms Used for " Spur "
Gear-wheel Teeth.

These are often formed by a machine-moulding process, and are known as " machine-moulded " types. They are satisfactory for comparatively slow speeds of rotation.

For high-class work, or high speeds of rotation, after the gears have been cast, the teeth are accurately machined to their true shape, and are known as " machine-cut " gears. Sometimes, however, gears are machine cut from solid " blank " discs of steel. For very high-class jobs the teeth are finished by grinding them to their final shape for accuracy.

Spur-gears may be made of cast iron, cast steel, forged steel, gun-metal, brass, or special alloys, etc. In order to reduce noise, gear pinions are sometimes made of layers of raw hide, compressed paper, vulcanite, or other special compositions, which are pressed together under very high pressure.

When made of raw hide, or compressed paper, fibre, etc., the outer edges are frequently fitted with a disc, made of brass or steel, on each of their sides, in order to give extra support and to prevent the edges of the fibre teeth from being distorted or pushed outwards sideways during use. Raw-hide or paper pinions are often coated with a mixture of glue substance, in order to enable them to resist wear and tear.

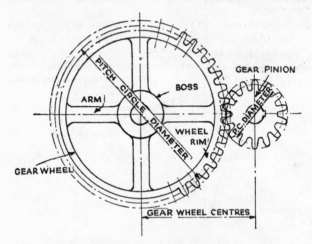

Fig. 103.—Typical " Spur " Gear-wheel and Pinion in " Mesh ".

Raw-hide or similar pinions are used extensively on electric motors which are used for driving gear-wheels of machines with which they are meshed.

Gear-wheel teeth must be properly meshed together—that is to say, the teeth must interlock correctly. In order to achieve this, the " pitch circle " of each wheel (gear wheel and pinion) must intersect, so as to provide a clearance at the top of the tooth of one wheel, and a space at the base between two teeth of the other wheel with which it is meshed. In order to ascertain the true position, *half* of the pitch-circle diameter dimension of each wheel must be added together, and the sum of these two dimensions gives the correct working " centres " of the two wheels.

If the wheels are positioned at a distance in excess of their correct centres, it will be appreciated that only a reduced length of the teeth will be in mesh, which increases the " leverage ", and the teeth may break off.

The formations of gear-wheel teeth are so arranged that during the rotation one tooth fully bears on the one of the

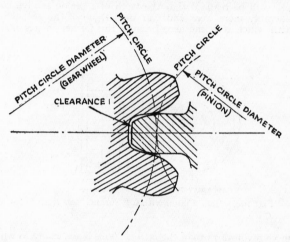

Fig. 103a.—Enlarged View Showing Teeth when " Meshed " Together.

Note.—Intersection of Pitch Circle diameters.

wheel with which it is meshed, until such time as the adjacent one takes up full contact (due to the rotation). The latter then takes up the drive just as the preceding tooth disengages. Therefore, in practice, two teeth of one wheel are always bearing on the two teeth of the other wheel at any time during the wheel's rotation. This will be seen on referring to Fig. 103.

Fig. 103a shows an enlarged diagram of a pinion-tooth in its correct position between two teeth of a gear-wheel. The clearance at the top of the tooth is also indicated.

The width of a gear-wheel tooth is usually two to three times the distance of the pitch. The width of a pinion is usually slightly more than that.

In order to give additional strength to gear-wheel teeth the rim is sometimes extended to the top of the teeth. This extension may be on one side or both sides of the teeth, and is called a " shroud " (see Fig. 104). A shroud is frequently fitted to a pinion, but the width of the pinion-teeth is then made similar to that of the gear-wheel, or slightly wider.

It will be realised that the teeth of a pinion receive considerably more wear and tear than those of the gear-wheel with which it is meshed, because the former makes many

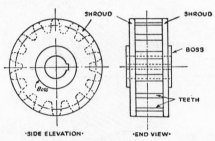

Fig. 104.—Gear Pinion with a " Shroud " on Both Sides.

more revolutions than the latter. This is especially so when the " gear ratio " is great. By this term it is meant that if a gear-wheel has forty teeth, and its corresponding pinion has ten teeth, the gear ratio is then forty to ten—*i.e.* four to one—which indicates that for every one revolution the gear-wheel makes, the pinion makes four revolutions. Therefore a pinion must be of robust construction, so it is often " shrouded ", made of tougher material than that of the gear-wheel, or its teeth may be wider. A gear-wheel may be made of cast iron, and its mating pinion of steel.

RAW-HIDE, PAPER, OR FIBRE PINION (Fig. 105)

Raw-hide or similar types of pinions are made from highly compressed layers of the material (raw-hide, paper, or fibre, etc.) which are also glued together. At both sides of the pinion, brass or steel plates are placed, which are secured by long rivets, passing completely through both the material and the side-plates. The rivets are usually countersunk at both ends.

When used in conjunction with gear-wheels the raw-hide teeth of these pinions are wider than the teeth of the gear-wheels. This is to ensure that the metal of the gear-wheel teeth does not contact the pinion metal side-plates, or the object of this design—which is to reduce the noise of metal to metal—would be defeated. It is therefore usual to allow for a quarter of an inch of extra width of the raw-hide, fibre, or paper, on each side, *more* than the *width* of the *gear-wheel teeth*.

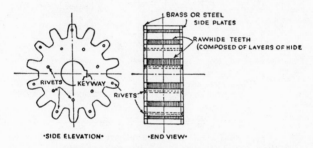

Fig. 105.—" Raw-hide " Gear Pinion.

HELICAL-GEARS (Figs. 106 and 107)

These differ from spur-gears on account of the teeth being set at an angle or incline from the centre lines, but the cross-section of the teeth is similar to the spur type. By inclining the teeth, a greater width is obtained for them, whilst the width of the rim is unaltered.

The pinion of a " helical "-gear must be " opposite handed " to the gear-wheel. This means that, if the teeth of a helical gear-wheel are of right-hand formation, those of the pinion must be left-handed, because the wheels revolve in opposite directions.

A disadvantage to the use of *single* helical teeth is that a *side pressure* is exerted, which causes a tendency to push each wheel out of mesh sideways. This also causes undue " *thrust* " on the bearings of the gear-shafts. In order to overcome this objection "double" helical gears are often used. These are of herring-bone pattern, the teeth being of V formation, which design retains the wheels in a central position, and thus obviates side thrust.

Illustrations of both "single" and "double" helical gears are shown in Figs. 106 and 107, from which the shapes of the teeth will be seen.

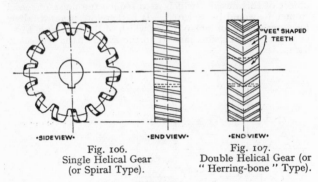

Fig. 106.
Single Helical Gear
(or Spiral Type).

Fig. 107.
Double Helical Gear (or
" Herring-bone " Type).

BEVEL-GEARS (Figs. 108 and 109)

When two shafts have their axes set at right angles to each other, the shafts may be "driven", or rotated by the use of "bevel"-gears. If it is desired to rotate one shaft at a different speed from the other, a bevel gear-wheel and bevel pinion would be used.

The shape of a bevel-wheel (or pinion) somewhat resembles that of a truncated cone. The formation of the teeth taper towards a central point in such a manner that if lines are continued from the outside edges of the teeth they would intersect at a point as shown in the illustration.

The pitch of the individual teeth of both the bevel-wheel and pinion must be equal, and the pitch-circle diameter of a bevel-pinion relative to its "mating" bevel-wheel is dependent on the gear ratio desired.

That is to say, if the bevel-"pinion" shaft is to rotate at a speed of four times that of the bevel-"wheel" shaft, the former must have a pitch-circle diameter of one quarter that of the latter. The number of teeth formed on the pinion and gear-wheel must also be in the same "ratio".

The formation of the cross-section of a bevel-gear tooth is

similar to that of a spur-gear type, but the length of the face
of the former tapers in such a manner that were it continued

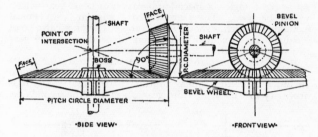

Fig. 108.—Bevel Gears (Wheel and Pinion in Mesh)
(90° Type).

to the point of intersection it would gradually diminish in
size and finally terminate at that point, as mentioned earlier,
and as will be seen from the illustration.

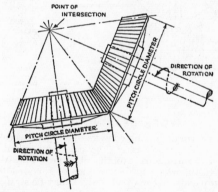

Fig. 109.—" Angular " Bevel Gears (in Mesh).

Bevel-gears are used for driving two shafts with axes at
right angles to each other at different speeds, but bevel-
wheels of *equal* diameter can be used for driving two shafts in

a similar position at *equal* speeds. When used thus, they are called " *mitre* "-gears.

If it is necessary to rotate two shafts whose axes are not set at right angles, a special application of bevel gear-wheels would be used. These are called " angular ", a typical example of which is shown in Fig. 109. They may also be of " equal " or " unequal " diameters, depending on the gear ratio desired for the relative shaft speeds.

It will be appreciated that when using gears for shaft-driving the two shafts concerned rotate in *opposite* directions. In order to obtain similar rotation to the first shaft, it is necessary to " mesh " a third gear-wheel with the second one.

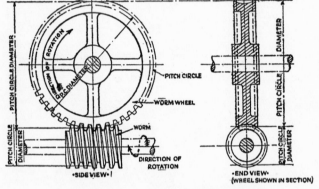

Fig. 110.—Worm and Worm-wheel (in Mesh).

WORM-GEARING (Fig. 110)

Another form of gearing consists of a " gear-wheel " and a " worm ". The worm is of " helical " or " spiral " shape, forming a " continuous " tooth. The gear-wheel has independent teeth, which are sometimes of rounded formation at their top ends, but in other designs may be straight.

The " worm " is mounted on a shaft, and is " meshed " with the " gear-wheel " mounted on another shaft and positioned at right angles to the former, as shown in the illustration. As the worm is rotated it " drives " the gear-wheel, different teeth of the latter coming into contact with the continuous " tooth " formation of the worm.

The worm is usually made of solid steel, but the gear-wheel is mostly made of phosphor-bronze or gun-metal, or at least its " rim and teeth " are made of those alloys. Such materials " blend " or " work together " better for that type of gear.

From the illustration it will be realised that the " drive " is developed by the worm-tooth formation, sliding into the spaces between the gear-wheel teeth, and the worm, being of " spiral " formation, thrusts forward, or " drives " the gear-wheel teeth.

It is therefore essential that the teeth of both the gear-wheel and the worm be accurately machined to their true formations. Owing to the sideways sliding action of the meshing of the teeth, efficient lubrication must also be provided.

When worm-gearing is used, a large " gear ratio " can be achieved. Gear ratios of 40 to 1 up to 60 to 1 are common. The system is used extensively for obtaining a speed reduction from electric motors—in one " step "—for the direct driving of various types of industrial machinery that require only comparatively slow speeds of rotation. This is a great advantage over ordinary " spur "-gearing, where the usual limit of ratio is 5 to 1 or 6 to 1.

It will be appreciated that in order to reduce the speed of an electric motor—which is in the region of, say, 1,000 revolutions per minute—down to the speed of an industrial machine, of 40 r.p.m., several " trains " of gears would have to be employed if spur-gearing were to be used. Such speed reductions can therefore more easily be achieved by the use of one set of worm reduction gear. The use of worm reduction gear also eliminates all the various shafts and bearings, etc. required for " spur-gearing ".

Worm reduction gears are mostly supplied in cast-iron dust-proof casings—as one complete unit—which results in a very compact job for the complete drive.

" RACK "-AND-PINION GEAR (Fig. 111)

This is a small pinion of the " spur "-toothed kind, which is employed in conjunction with a flat row of teeth called a " rack ". The rack might be compared with the rim of a large spur gear-wheel laid out flat.

Such gearing is often employed for operating " weir "-gate valves, and for operating doors of large storage bins or hoppers.

For such use the rack is bolted to the back of the door, and is free to slide in guides. The pinion is fixed in position, but is free to rotate. It is keyed to a spindle, on which is fitted either a " hand-wheel " or chain and sprocket-wheel. When the pinion is rotated, its teeth being meshed with those of the rack, the latter moves along, thus operating the door-plate to which it is attached. When used for this purpose both the rack and pinion are usually made of cast iron, and the teeth do not require machining, but they would be machined for higher classes of work.

This type of gear is also employed to give a sliding motion to parts of machinery where a regulated control of the to-and-

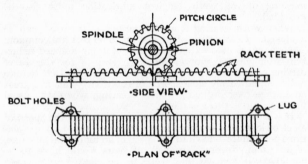

Fig. 111.—" Rack " and Pinion.

fro motion is required, such as " machine tools ", shaping machines, drilling machines, etc.

CHAIN-WHEEL GEARS

General

A " chain "-wheel is one which has narrow teeth suitably formed to fit into the links of a chain, and is employed in conjunction with a chain.

This type of gearing is used extensively in engineering of all kinds—from bicycles up to heavy industrial plant " drives ". Instead of the teeth of chain-wheels being " meshed " together, as in the case of spur and bevel gears, they are connected by means of an endless chain. Many different forms

of chains are used; one of the most common is the " roller "
type, invariably used for bicycles.

An advantage of the " chain " drive is that two shafts
spaced a large distance apart can be driven by chain connection. It is also " positive ", there being no possibility of
" slip " occurring, as with a belt drive.

Furthermore, if wheels of different diameters are used,
corresponding " gear ratios " can be achieved—within certain
limits, of course—and three or more shafts, whose axes are
parallel, can be driven off one single chain. This principle is
sometimes used for operating the valve-timing gears of motor-
car engines. The usual limit for the gear ratio of chain drives
is 6 to 1, but in certain cases ratios of 8 to 1 have been used
with success.

High-class roller chains can be run at a velocity of
365·760 m. (1,200) to 457,200 m. (1,500 feet) per minute under
certain conditions, and where suitable lubrication is provided.

An inclined or horizontal position is preferable for the
" centres " of the drive. The " tight " side (or " driving "
strand) of the roller chain should be the *uppermost* wherever
possible. For high speeds the chain should be kept
reasonably tight, and, once " stretched ", should be dis-
carded, owing to the danger of its rollers not " bedding
down " between the sprocket teeth correctly, and possibly
breaking them off, or the chain itself may break.

In addition to the " pitched-roller " chain, other kinds are
used. The " detachable-link " malleable-iron type is used
for industrial plants, light-type conveyors, elevators, etc.,
but these must run at much lower peripheral speeds.

Specially designed chains are used for heavy industrial
plants, dredger work, etc. These are of very robust construction, and their links are connected by *hard-steel* pins of the
bolt type.

Let us next consider in detail the various kinds.

Sprocket-wheel and Chain (Heavy Industrial Type) (Fig. 112)

The illustration (Fig. 112) depicts a type which, in addition
to being used for geared drives, is used for industrial plants,
such as " double-strand " chain conveyors and elevators.
The side links can then be used to carry " attachments " for
securing the conveyor " buckets " or " bars ", etc., such as
are frequently used for coal and coke conveyors.

Sprocket wheels are usually made of cast iron or " malleable " iron. The chains are made of steel, and their rollers
and pins are case-hardened to resist wear. All types of

chains require lubrication of some description. Oil is usually used.

The " pitch " of a chain is the distance between the centres of the rollers, and the " pitch " of a sprocket wheel is the same distance measured between the centres of the teeth *at the " pitch circle "*.

The type of chain illustrated is suitable for speeds of from 15·240 m. to 36·576 m. (50 to 120 feet) per minute.

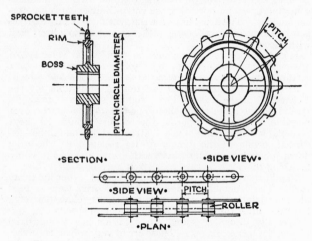

Fig. 112.—Sprocket-wheel and Roller Chain (Heavy Industrial Type).

Chain-wheel and Chain (Close-pitch Roller Chain (Figs. 113, 113a, and 113b)

The " close-pitch " roller chain is used chiefly for driving machinery and for achieving the gear ratios between the " motive power unit " and the machine. This type of chain is of high grade, and can be used for relatively high speeds when used in conjunction with suitable " wheels ", and if lubricated effectively.

The large wheel for such a " drive " is called a " *chain-wheel* ", and the smaller wheel is called the " *chain-pinion* ", and gear ratios of up to 6 to 1 or 8 to 1 can be used, but the latter should not be exceeded.

This class of chain is of light but strong construction, and is supplied in various sizes to suit the horse-powers of the drives concerned. It is of all-steel construction, and its components are case-hardened, and may be treated to resist corrosion. Roller chains require efficient lubrication, and in some cases they run in an " oil-bath ". The wheels used with close-pitch roller chains are often made of steel, and their teeth are also " case-hardened ".

A typical " close-pitch " roller chain is shown in Fig. 113a, from which it will be seen the rollers are mounted on " bushes " (or small cylinders) through which pass the link-connecting pins. These carry the inner and outer side-links, and the pins have their ends " pressed over " or " riveted " in order to secure the links.

Normally, in order to shorten or lengthen a " close-pitch " roller chain, the process involves the removal or addition of two or more links (for if an " inner " *one* only is removed, two outer links remain, which cannot be connected). To over-come this difficulty in cases where only one link has to be removed or added to give the desired chain length, a special " cranked link " has to be used. This is depicted in Fig. 113b. When two inner-links require connecting by an outer one, a special spring type connecting link can be used.

The pins of the special link are made with recesses on one end of each, into which fits the " spring clip ". Such an arrangement obviates the necessity of riveting the pins' ends, and also facilitates disconnecting them when the occasion arises. The " spring clip " must always be fitted with its closed end in the foremost direction of travel (see Fig. 113c).

All chain drives should be arranged, preferably, so that their centres are either " inclined " or " horizontal ". A " vertical " drive should be avoided wherever possible.

A long chain should, if possible, be provided with some tensioning device, in order to keep it reasonably tight. The term " centres " of a chain drive means the dimension between the centres of the two sprocket wheels (" wheel " and " pinion "), as shown in Fig. 113d. A chain drive can be utilised for driving three or more chain-wheels, each attached to separate shafts, as shown in the diagram (Fig. 113e).

Furthermore, should the centres of the drive be essentially of a fixed nature, when the chain wears, a tensioning device can be employed by fixing another small wheel at some con-venient position along the strand of the chain. The small wheel, called a " jockey "-wheel, is fitted into a suitable

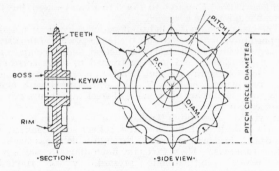

Fig. 113.—Chain-wheel (for " Close Pitch " Roller Chain).

Fig. 113a.—" Close Pitch " Roller Chain.

Inner Link.　　Fig. 113b.　　" Cranked Link ".

 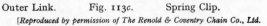

Outer Link.　　Fig. 113c.　　Spring Clip.

slide-frame, as shown. By adjusting the screw, the
" jockey "-wheel is pushed bodily along the slide-frame, and

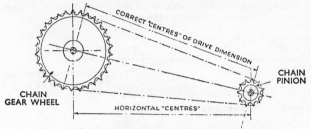

Fig. 113*d*.—Typical Chain " Drive " Arrangement.

thus " tensions " (or tightens) the chain. The " jockey "
wheel rotates idly on its spindle, and is kept in the desired
place by securing the " lock-nut " of the adjusting screw.

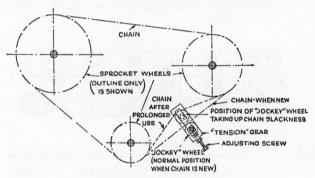

Fig. 113*e*.—Chain " Drive " for Three Wheels and Fitted
with " Jockey "-wheel Tensioning Device.

By this means a chain-drive can be kept operating successfully
for long periods, but when a considerable amount of wear
has taken place, so as to cause the links to gear inaccurately
with the teeth of the main wheels, it should be replaced.

In addition to the " jockey "-wheel tension gear, other kinds are often used. Of these, the " automatic " type shown in Fig. 113f is used extensively. It comprises a " spring-steel slipper " bar, curved to a desired shape, with a coil-type " tension " spring attached to each end.

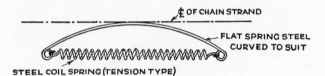

Fig. 113f.—Automatic Chain Tensioning Device
(" Bent-bow " Type).

The curved bar presses on the back of the chain, and as the latter stretches or slackens, the tension of the coil-spring increases the curve of the bar. In doing so it presses on to the chain and keeps it tight.

So far all the chains described have been what are termed

Fig. 113g.—" Duplex " Roller Chain.
[Reproduced by permission of The Renold & Coventry Chain Co., Ltd.

" single-strand " kinds. Other types of " close-pitch " roller chains are often used, known as " duplex " (see Fig. 113g) or " triplex " pattern (see Fig. 113h). These are composed of two (for duplex)—three (for triplex)—single strands assembled side by side, but each set of links is connected by a pin which projects completely through the whole assembly, thus securing together the two or three strands.

The use of such arrangements permits the transmission of much higher powers than a single-strand chain of the same " pitch ". Special wheels have to be used for these chains, having two or three rows of teeth, side by side, respectively.

The chief advantage gained by using duplex or triplex strand chains is that a closer pitch is obtained; thus more teeth are in mesh with the chain on each wheel than if a larger or stouter chain of single strand were to be used to transmit the same power load. A triplex roller chain of 25·4 mm. (1-inch pitch) can be used for transmitting 140 cheval vapeur (HP) at a " pinion speed " of 1,200 r.p.m., whereas a much stouter chain of single strand, and involving a larger pitch, would have to be used to replace the triplex type.

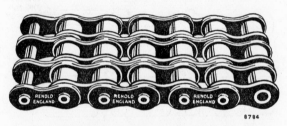

Fig. 113*h*.—" Triplex " Roller Chain.

[*Reproduced by permission of The Renold & Coventry Chain Co., Ltd.*]

Detachable Link Chain (Fig. 114)

This chain has links shaped so that each can be easily detached, and it can thus be quickly made up to any desired length. Further, after prolonged use, when " stretch " has developed, the chain can easily be shortened, by detaching one or more links. This is effected by merely tilting one link at right angles to an adjacent one, which permits it to be detached by sliding sideways through the " recess " shown in Fig. 114.

Detachable link type chains are usually made of " malleable iron ", which is comparatively ductile. It is far less brittle than ordinary cast iron—which could not be used for chain links, owing to its being weak in tension. Ordinary cast iron or steel " sprocket " wheels are used.

These chains are employed for " drives " of comparatively

low speeds, and for work of less importance. For " conveyor " and " elevator " construction, to which they lend themselves, special " lugs " are cast on one or both sides of some of the links, through which can be bolted the elevator " buckets " at the required intervals along the chain. These lugs are called " attachments ", and may be of various formations to suit the nature of the work.

" Detachable link " chains are made in a large number of sizes for industrial work, for conveyors and elevators used for gravel, sand, or " coal-handling " plants, etc.

Fig. 114*a* shows a typical " link " with an " attachment " lug on each side, to which an " elevator bucket " may be

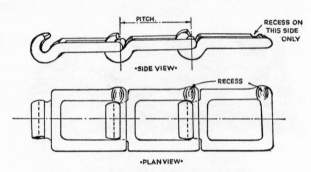

Fig. 114.—" Detachable Link " Type Chain.

[Reproduced by permission of Ewart Chainbelt Co., Ltd.

bolted. Such " attachments " are referred to in the trade by various letters and numbers for each particular kind of formation, which differ for various classes of work. The kind illustrated is known as " K2 " type, and is perhaps one of the most common.

These chains require to be assembled and fitted to the " driving " sprocket-wheel in such a manner that the wheel teeth, as they rotate, tend to " close up " the " hooks " of the links, and the spaces are filled by the links preceding them. If used otherwise the pull in the chain would tend to open the hooks, and the " tensile stress " thus developed might cause them to break (see Fig. 114*b*).

The *lower* " strand " of *this* type of chain should, wherever

possible, be arranged to form the " driving " side or " tight "
side.   This ensures that the pull will not allow it to sag.

The upper strand will then sag, and in doing so forms a

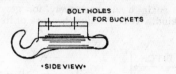

Fig. 114*a*.—" K2 " Type Link for Detachable Link Chain.

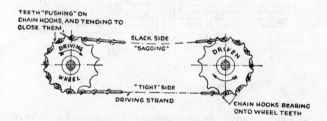

Fig. 114*b*.—Correct Method of Driving by a Malleable
Detachable Link Chain.

better " arc of contact " over the sprocket-wheels, which
thus derive the benefit from the larger number of teeth in
mesh with the chain.

With all " chain drives " the wheel which is " power

driven " from its shaft is termed the " driving " or " driver "
wheel, whilst the other wheel—connected by the chain—
is called the " driven " one.

" Silent " or " Noiseless " Chain (Fig. 115)

Another chain used extensively for gear drives is the
" silent " kind. It is so called because of its quiet running,

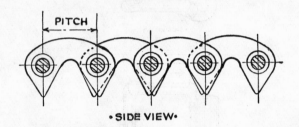

• SIDE VIEW•

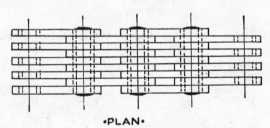

•PLAN•

Fig. 115.—" Silent " Chain

even when moving at high speeds. This chain has links of
special form, as shown in the illustration.

Each link is free to " swivel " about its " pin ", and when
passing over a gear-wheel it takes up a formation as shown in
Fig. 115a. The chain-link teeth merely " slide " into
position on the sprocket-wheel, and therefore cause practically
no noise whatever.

A chain of this character can be made up to any suitable
width in order to cater for the horse-power of the drive con-

cerned, and various sizes are made of convenient " pitch " to
suit the nature of different jobs. " Silent " chains are very
effective, and claim up to 98 per cent. efficiency.

The wheels employed resemble " spur-gear " teeth, by their
having flat, wide faces. The chains are made of hardened
steel of similar quality to that used for roller-type chains.
They wear very well indeed, for the only parts which experi-
ence much friction are the " pin " joints.

Silent chains, in addition to being used extensively for
heavy industrial machinery " drives ", are also frequently
used for " timing "-gear drives of motor-car engines, etc.

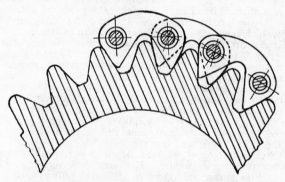

Fig. 115a.—Enlarged View Showing Application of Chain
Links to Wheel Teeth.

Belt and Rope Types of Gearing and " Drives " (General)

Perhaps one of the oldest types of " gearing " or " drive "
is that effected by an endless belt passed over two pulleys.
The pulleys may be of equal or unequal diameter, depending
on the " gear ratio " required. Originally leather was used
for the construction of the belt, but of later years belts have
been formed of woven cotton " duck ", rubber, canvas, or
other pliable materials.

A flat belt drive may be of the " open " type or " crossed "
type. The latter is used in cases where one of the pulleys is
required to rotate in the opposite direction to the other.

Prior to the development of electric motors for individual
drive of each machine in a workshop, belts were used exten-

sively for driving machines from one common " line-shaft " on which several pulleys were mounted, one to drive each machine. The line-shaft itself was then driven from either a steam, oil, or gas engine. This practice is still maintained in some of the older factories, or in areas where no electricity supply is available.

Such drives rely entirely on the " frictional " grip of the belt on the pulleys, and it is therefore essential to keep the belt as tight as possible (within reason), in order to prevent " slip ".

Owing to the fact that leather is limited in its length (by the size of the animal from which it originated), for long belt drives it is necessary to join several lengths together. This is usually effected by either " splicing " the joint and securing it by " laces ", or by metal clips—known as " belt-fasteners " —of which there are many different kinds in existence.

Rope " drives " consist of one or more cotton (or cotton and hemp) ropes of circular cross-section. These are used in conjunction with pulleys which have their rims " grooved " to accommodate the ropes. This class of drive was originally used extensively in mills and factories in the Lancashire and Yorkshire industrial areas, but is being superseded by individual motor drives for each machine. The rope ends are usually joined together by splicing. The pulley grooves are of " rounded Vee " formation, which give a better grip by the ropes " wedging " into the " Vee ".

" Steel-wire " ropes are used for many purposes, but not so extensively for gearing. They are, however, used for hoists, lifts, and aerial ropeways, etc. The pulleys used for wire ropes are grooved, and the bases of the grooves are often lined with some softer material, such as leather, wood, etc., in order to prevent the wire from slipping, and also to avoid damaging it. Wire ropes are also extensively used for haulage work, in quarries, brickfields, collieries, etc.

" Vee belts " are used for modern " drives " and for gearing. These consist of rubber and canvas (or leather) bonded together and are of " Vee " cross-section. The pulleys used in conjunction with such belts have specially shaped " Vee grooves " formed in their rims. At one period this kind of belt was used extensively for motor-cycles, but it has since been superseded by the modern " chain " drive. They are, however, at present being used to an increasing degree for many industrial " drives ", for which purpose they are very efficient.

In some cases where multiple belts are used for the drive only the smaller pulley is grooved, for it has been found in practice, especially for short drives (those of small centre distances), that it is unnecessary to " groove " the larger pulley, owing to the tension of the drive maintaining the belts in true alignment.

Link-type belts are also used extensively. There are several varieties, and perhaps one of the oldest and best known is the " Whittle ", which consists of small leather links joined alternately by steel links. The individual links are easily detachable, so a belt of this description can readily be shortened—or lengthened—as required. Both the Whittle-type belt and the Vee belt are used for driving the " cooling fans " of motor-car engines. They are also used for many industrial drives.

Another modern type of belt drive is one composed of overlapping layers of leather (or rubber and canvas), in the form of individual " links ". These—like the Whittle—are also easily detached to form lengths of adjustable sizes. They are known as " laminated " link belts.

Each individual type will now be considered in detail.

Flat " Belt and Pulley " Gearing (Figs. 116b, 116c, and 116d)

This is composed of two pulleys, over which passes an endless belt. The pulley diameters determine the relative " gear ratios " of the drives, in a similar manner to those of " chain-drives " previously described. The pulleys may be of cast iron if they are of comparatively small diameters (see Fig. 116).

For pulleys of large diameter, however, the rims are composed of wrought iron or mild steel, and have cast iron bosses (or hubs), from which project mild-steel " arms " of circular cross-section (Fig. 116a). These " arms " are secured into the " boss ", and their opposite ends are reduced, passed through the rim, and riveted or " burred over ". The belt used should be slightly narrower than the pulley " face " width.

Pulleys may be either of one-piece formation or of the " split " type. Fig. 116 shows a " *one-piece* " cast-iron pulley, and Fig. 116a a " split "-type wrought-iron pulley with a cast-iron boss, the latter also being of the split pattern (or in two halves). The split type has the advantage that it can be unbolted and fitted into position on a shaft without disturbing the bearings, etc. The " faces " of pulleys are " crowned "—or " curved slightly "—which causes the belt to run centrally and keep in line.

With the " open "-type drive, as shown in Fig. 116b, both pulleys rotate in the same direction, and it is advantageous, whenever possible, to use the lower " strand " of the belt for the " driving " (or tight) side. By this means a greater

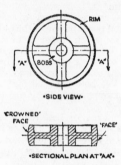

Fig. 116.—Cast Iron Pulley.

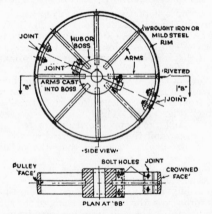

Fig. 116a.—Wrought Iron or Mild Steel Pulley with Cast Iron Boss (Split Type).

" arc of contact " is obtained over the rims of the pulleys, similar to the arrangement described earlier for " *detachable-link* " *chain drives.*

This is caused by the top side (or strand) of the belt
"sagging" (due to its weight and slackness), which permits
it to lie over more pulley rim surface area, as will clearly be

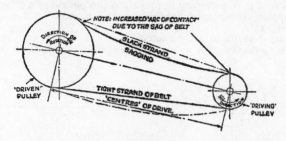

Fig. 116b.—Open Type Belt Drive (for a " Flat "
Type Belt).

seen from the diagram (Fig. 116b). The opposite would be
the result, as shown in dotted lines on the diagram, if the
TOP strand of belt were used for the driving side, as the

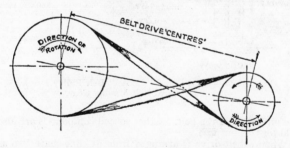

Fig. 116c.—" Crossed " Flat Belt Drive.
Note.—Pulleys rotate in opposite directions.

bottom one would then " sag " away from the pulley rims,
thereby losing contact surface or *reducing* the arc of contact.
Flat belt-drives of the " open " type should always have
their " drive centres " either horizontal or inclined. They

should *never* be vertical, for if so arranged the " centrifugal " force developed, combined with the force of gravity, causes the belt to stretch and leave the rim of the lower pulley, thereby losing contact with its rim surface.

Should it be necessary to rotate the two pulleys of a drive in opposite directions, a flat belt may be " crossed ", as shown in Fig. 116c.

Flat belt-drives are sometimes inclined to " slip ". In order to prevent this, an application of resin may be given to

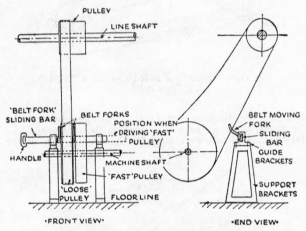

Fig. 116d.—" Fast " and " Loose " Belt Pulley Drive showing Typical Belt Moving Gear.

the underside of the belt. Other special compounds are also sold for this purpose.

When a belt-drive is arranged from a " line-shaft " so as to drive a machine it may be necessary to rotate the machine intermittently, without having to " start " and " stop " the line-shaft each time. This can be accomplished by fitting what are known as " fast-and-loose " pulleys to the machine-shaft. The term " fast-and-loose " pulleys indicates that the " *fast* " one is securely " keyed " to the machine shaft, but the " *loose* " pulley is fitted with a gun-metal or brass bush, and is allowed to rotate freely, being driven from the constantly rotating "line-shaft" or "power" shaft. The width of the pulley face of the latter, however, must be at least equal to the combined widths of both the "fast" and "loose" pulleys. The loose pulley is retained in position on the machine-shaft by fitting a "loose collar", which thus prevents sideways movement, and the three pulleys must all be lined up truly, as shown in the front view of Fig. 116d.

In order to slide the belt from the loose pulley position to the fast one, so as to bring the machine into motion, a belt-moving gear (sometimes called belt-"striking" or "shifting" gear) is used. This consists of a flat bar free to slide in a suitable guide-frame. Mounted on the bar are two "forks", which are arranged so as to just "span" the belt width, and they must, of course, be fitted to the oncoming belt-strand.

By moving the fork slide-bar, the belt can be guided from the loose pulley on to the fast one, and thus set the machine in motion, or vice versa. Suitable "stops" are fitted to the slide-bar to retain it in its relative position.

As the fast pulley is the one which has to cater for the power drive, it is essential for it to be placed close up to the machine shaft-bearing, whilst the loose pulley, not having to cater for the power drive, can be outermost, or "overhung".

Belt Joints (Figs. 117 to 126)

Many devices are used for the joints of belts. The earlier leather types of belt were often joined by "lacing" together their lapped ends, or by the use of soft copper rivets. Later, other types were developed, consisting of various forms of soft steel clips, or plates.

For thin, small belts, where the drive is of a light character only, it is sufficient merely to stitch together the various lengths which are assembled to make up a complete belt. This can be done by hand, or by the industrial type of sewing-machine as used by saddlers and leather merchants. Waxed thread of stout formation is used for hand-stitched work, and strong thread or "flax twine" is used for machine-stitching. The ends to be joined are cut to form a "splice", and are often glued prior to stitching them together.

For heavier and thicker types of belts a similar glued spliced joint is used, but instead of stitching, the joint is laced together with stout leather laces, which somewhat resemble heavy leather boot-laces, but are of course much stronger. The laces are sometimes dressed with tallow in order to make them more durable. A joint of this description is shown in Fig. 117.

F

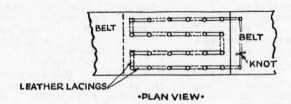

Fig. 117.—" Laced " Joint for Flat Leather Belt.

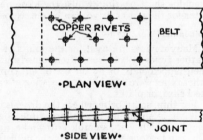

Fig. 118.—Spliced and Riveted Joint for Flat Leather Belt.

Copper rivets are sometimes used in conjunction with small copper washers. The rivet-heads are slightly countersunk, which permits them to penetrate well into the leather, so that the outer faces of the heads lie almost flush with the belt face. Copper washers are placed over the opposite ends of the rivets, which are then burred over by hammering to clench them. This joint is depicted in Fig. 118.

Joints of the " butt " pattern are also frequently used for belting, instead of the lapped splice kind. This only involves cutting the belt ends dead square, then using one of the approved kinds of metal fasteners. A fastener is shown in Fig. 119. It comprises several metal clips or staples which

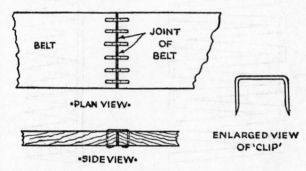

Fig. 119.—" Clip " or " Staple " Type of Joint for Flat Leather Belt.

are driven through the belt-ends. Afterwards the pointed ends are hammered flat into the underside of the belt.

An improved type of fastener is shown in Fig. 120, which consists of a soft steel plate, pressed out and bent to form a series of continuous clips. This is a handy form, and very easily fitted.

Another form of belt-fastener which is largely used is the " Alligator " type shown in Fig. 121. It consists of a series of interlocking, hook-shaped links, through which passes a hinge-pin, and it is only necessary to cut the belt-ends dead square and hammer the hooks into the belt.

A further well-known belt-fastener is the " Bristol ", which is shown in Fig. 122. In principle it closely resembles that shown in Fig. 120, but the " points " are staggered, and thus form two rows of spikes, one on each side of the belt-joint. After driving the spikes through the belt from the

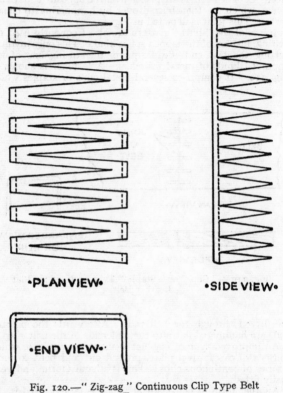

·PLAN VIEW·   ·SIDE VIEW·

·END VIEW··

Fig. 120.—" Zig-zag " Continuous Clip Type Belt Fastener.

top side, they are " clenched " similar to the clips shown in the side view of Fig. 119.

One of the earlier kinds of belt-fastener is shown in Fig. 123. It consists of a slightly curved plate, from which project

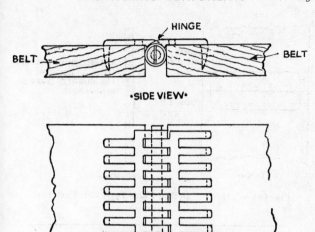

HINGE

BELT   BELT

•SIDE VIEW•

HINGE PIN

•PLAN VIEW•

Fig. 121.—" Alligator " Type Belt Fastener.

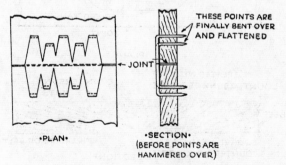

THESE POINTS ARE
FINALLY BENT OVER
AND FLATTENED

JOINT

•PLAN•

•SECTION•
(BEFORE POINTS ARE
HAMMERED OVER)

Fig. 122.—" Bristol " Type Belt Fastener.

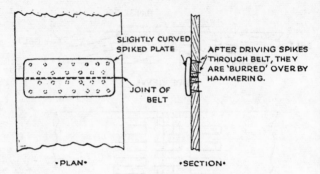

SLIGHTLY CURVED SPIKED PLATE

AFTER DRIVING SPIKES THROUGH BELT, THEY ARE 'BURRED' OVER BY HAMMERING.

JOINT OF BELT

•PLAN•

•SECTION•

Fig. 123.—" Harris " Spiked Plate Type Belt Fastener.

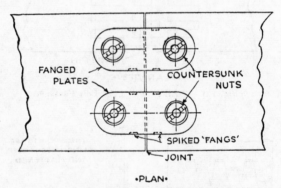

FANGED PLATES

COUNTERSUNK NUTS

SPIKED 'FANGS'

JOINT

•PLAN•

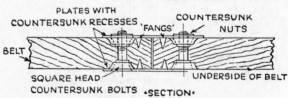

PLATES WITH COUNTERSUNK RECESSES

'FANGS'

COUNTERSUNK NUTS

BELT

SQUARE HEAD COUNTERSUNK BOLTS

UNDERSIDE OF BELT

•SECTION•

Fig. 124.—Bolted " Fang-plate " Type Belt Fastener.

spikes—similar to a large metal shoe "*protector*". After the spikes have been driven through the belt they are burred over, or riveted. This type, known as the "Harris" spiked plate, was used originally for leather belts, but of recent years it has been largely superseded by the foregoing metal-clip patterns.

Fig. 124 shows the bolted "fang-plate" type, from which it will be seen that it comprises two thin metal plates from which spikes project along the sides. At each end of the plates recesses are formed to accommodate countersunk bolts and nuts. As an alternative to this pattern, plain flat plates

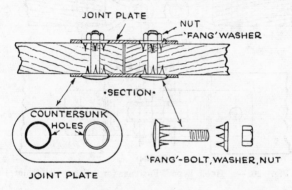

Fig. 125.—"Fang-bolt" and Plate Type Belt Fastener.

are sometimes used in conjunction with "fang" bolts and "fang" washers, as shown in Fig. 125.

Still another form is depicted in Fig. 126. This is the link or hook type originally used extensively for the belt drives of motor-cycles. It has also been used to a fairly large extent for light-type belt-drives for industrial purposes—chiefly for driving small high-speed grinding-wheels, etc.

In addition to leather belts, other types are extensively used, which are rapidly replacing the former; woven canvas is one. Canvas is sometimes interwoven with camel-hair and other substances. A special composition of a "gummy" nature—known as "Balata"—is now extensively used for impregnating the canvas, giving the belt more durability.

One of the chief advantages of the woven belt is that it can be made in lengths and widths of various sizes, whereas leather has to be " jointed " to form a long belt. A disadvantage, however, is that the plain canvas-woven types are affected by the weather; therefore they cannot be used successfully for outdoor purposes unless treated with weather-proof coatings or impregnated with " Balata ", as mentioned above. Most of the previously described belt-fasteners can

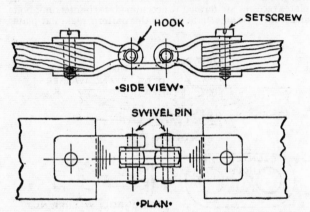

Fig. 126.— " Hook Type " Fastener for " Vee " Belt Joint.

be used for either type of belt, but the lapped-" laced " and lapped-" copper-riveted " joints are not used for woven-type belts.

Link-type Leather Belts (Fig. 127)

Leather belts are sometimes made in " link " form—*i.e.* a complete belt is composed of a number of links. These are made from small pieces of leather of equal size, interlocked and secured together by steel pins, as shown in Fig. 127. Such belts can be made to suit any length of " drive " or any suitable width.

A belt of this class is often used for the main " drive " of a line-shaft driven by an engine, or for driving a dynamo, etc. It can be easily shortened or lengthened by filing off the " burred " ends from the pins and detaching or attaching the requisite number of links and re-jointing it.

•SIDE VIEW•

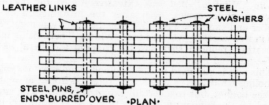

LEATHER LINKS   STEEL WASHERS

STEEL PINS, ENDS 'BURRED' OVER   •PLAN•

Fig. 127.—Leather Link-type Flat Belt.

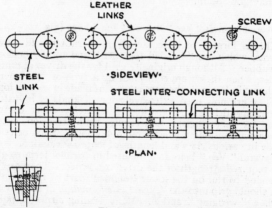

LEATHER LINKS   SCREW

STEEL LINK   •SIDEVIEW•

STEEL INTER-CONNECTING LINK

•PLAN•

CROSS SECTION OF LINKS

Fig. 128.—" Whittle " Leather Belt (for Use in Grooved Pulleys.)

" Whittle " Leather Link Belt (Fig. 128)

This is another kind which makes use of small strips of leather in order to form a complete belt. It is, however, for use in conjunction with " Vee " grooved pulleys, and consists of kidney-shaped strips of leather, screwed together.

Steel inter-connecting links are used alternately, and have " lugs " formed at each end so as to " couple-up " with the leather links. The complete link is secured together by means of the screw, and any suitable number of links can be used to form the required belt length. No special fastener is required, and when a belt stretches it can easily be shortened by merely detaching one or more links.

The " Whittle " belt was extensively used for the main drive of motor-cycles, even after the introduction of the rubber-and-canvas " Vee " belt, for the latter was inclined to slip in wet weather, whereas the " Whittle " belt, being made of leather, reduced such slip by gripping the metal of the " Vee-grooved " pulleys far better.

This belt is still used in the automobile industry for engine " cooling fan-drives ", which are protected from the weather by the bonnet, but to a certain extent it is now being superseded by the rubber-and-canvas type. It is, however, used for many industrial drives for belt speeds up to approximately 466·800 m. (3,500 feet) per minute.

Rubber-and-canvas " Vee " Belt or " Vee " Rope (Fig. 129)

This is formed of alternate layers of rubber and woven canvas, which are " bonded together " and totally enclosed by rubber. Although originally used for the drives of motor-cycles, when they were connected by a type of " fastener ", as shown in Fig. 126, they are at present made in endless form.

They are now used extensively for all kinds of industrial machinery drives and gearing of relatively short centres. They are very efficient, and require little attention, except occasional tensioning when stretch develops. Such belts are made in various sizes and lengths of looped formation.

Several " Vee " belts may be used in parallel form to give the required strength of the drive concerned. They are *not* intended to run on the lower (rounded) part of the grooves, but should grip into the " Vee " *side formation* of the grooves with a " wedging " action. Many leading firms of pulley manufacturers now stock standard sizes of pulleys grooved to suit any number of " Vee " belts of specified width and of certain popular gear ratios.

Such belts are used for quite high speeds, up to 1524·000 m. (5,000 feet) per minute, and are often used for electric motor drives, especially in cases where the motor can be mounted on slide rails to form the " tensioning " device. Multiples of such belts can be used in parallel forms for drives of up to 100 cheval vapeur (HP) and for gear ratios up to 8 to 1.

Instead of canvas being used in layers for Vee belts, nylon cord is now being used extensively.

Note.—Flat-type rubber-and-canvas belts are used universally for conveyor and elevator main conveying-belts, but not to a large extent as driving belts.

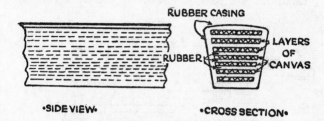

Fig. 129.—Rubber-and-canvas " Vee " Belt.

Laminated-link Leather Vee Belt (Fig. 129*b*)

Another interesting form of Vee belt (or Vee rope, as they are sometimes called) is the laminated-link pattern. It is composed of overlapping strips of pliable leather, each of a slightly tapered width, so that collectively a Vee shape is formed when assembled and in driving position, as shown in the section view of Fig. 129*b*.

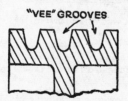

Fig. 129*a*.—Pulley Rim for " Vee " Belts.

Each link is provided with holes for the rivets. These holes are interconnected by slots, to enable the rivets to be slid along and extracted from the large hole when detaching any links. No special tools are required for assembling or dismantling, for these operations can be performed by hand. Such belts are therefore easily adjusted by detaching or adding more links as required. They are used extensively for industrial machinery drives, in conjunction with grooved pulleys similar to those shown for the endless rubber-and-canvas Vee belts in Fig. 129a.

Laminated Vee belts, in addition to being composed of

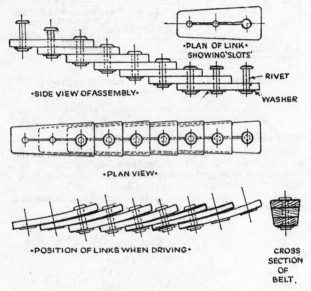

·PLAN OF LINK·
SHOWING 'SLOTS'

RIVET

·SIDE VIEW OF ASSEMBLY·

WASHER

·PLAN VIEW·

·POSITION OF LINKS WHEN DRIVING·

CROSS
SECTION
OF
BELT.

Fig. 129b.—Laminated Leather Link Type " Vee " Belt.

leather links, are now also obtainable with their links formed of rubber and canvas bonded together.

One of these—the " Whittle " laminated type—employs a novel fastener having a detachable head. It is made of manganese bronze, which has the strength of steel, and cannot rust or corrode.

The patent head is attached (or detached) merely by pressing it into the rubber, and turning through an angle of 90 degrees, when the shank end can be passed through the oval slot provided.

The head is securely locked in position, when the top of the shank fits into the recesses each side of the oval slot.

An illustration of the link assembly, together with views of the fastener details, are shown in Fig. 129c.

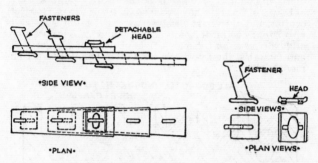

Fig. 129c.—" Whittle " Laminated Link Rubber-and-canvas " Vee " Belt.

[Reproduced by permission of T. Whittle & Sons, Ltd.

Cotton or Hemp Rope Gearing (Fig. 130)

Ropes formed of twisted strands of cotton, or hemp, are extensively used for gearing and drives in mills and various industrial factories, especially those of the textile and woollen trades. The strands of which the rope is composed may be twisted " right handed ", whilst the yarn of which the strands are made would be twisted " left handed ". When several strands are twisted together the resulting formation in cross-section is somewhat circular. The size of a rope is determined by the diameter of a circle which would just circumscribe the formation.

The pulleys used in conjunction with rope drives are grooved, so as to form a rounded Vee, and the ropes grip the sides of the Vee (except if used as guide pulleys, when they are rounded, and the ropes then rest on the base of the round grooves).

Ropes are used up to about 50·8 mm. (2 inches) in diameter, and up to twenty such ropes may be used for one drive, by having pulleys with the requisite number of grooves to suit. The most common number of strands which form one complete rope is three or sometimes four. The joints are formed by splicing the rope-ends together so as to form one endless loop.

The underside strands of the loops should be used for the driving side, similarly to a flat belt-drive. Thus large " arcs of contact " are given on the relative pulleys.

Drives of this type have been used up to 3·048 m. (100 feet) centres, and ropes have also been used successfully for speeds up to 1828·800 m. (6,000 feet) per minute. As ropes were originally used for the main drives of steam engines in mills and factories, the fly-wheels were often grooved to accommodate them.

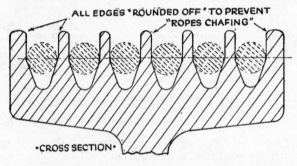

Fig. 130.—Typical Section of Grooved Pulley for Cotton Rope Drive.

The pulleys used should be of sufficient diameter so as to avoid bending the ropes unduly. One well-established rule recommends that the pulley diameter should be at least thirty times that of the rope concerned, so that if 50·80 mm. (2-inch)-diameter ropes are used, the minimum pulley diameter should be 1524·0 mm. (60 inches or 5 feet). The diameter of the pulley is measured from the position at which the rope wedges into the Vee groove formation.

Fig. 130 shows a pulley grooved for six ropes. The latter are shown in their relative positions when new. As wear takes place they lodge deeper into the grooves.

CHAPTER IX

PIPES OR TUBES, FITTINGS, CONNEC-
TIONS, JOINTS, GLANDS, VALVES,
ETC. (GENERAL)

PIPES, or tubes, are usually hollow, cylindrical-shaped components, although in certain cases they may be of rectangular or oval cross-section, examples being those used for air-conditioning ducts and sewage work respectively. They may be made of the following materials : cast iron, steel, wrought iron, copper, brass, aluminium, or other alloys, each depending on the work for which they are intended.

Several different types of connections are used for joining pipe lengths. Some may have what are called " spigot-and-socket " joints, whilst others have flanges either cast integral with the pipe or screwed on to each length. Pipes or tubes of small diameter, sometimes have unions or sockets directly screw-threaded on to them. Steel pipes may be joined merely by welding lengths together.

Various fittings are employed for pipe installations in order to form angle bends, branches, etc., and to provide for expansion. Valves often have to be fitted to regulate the flow of a pipe's contents, or to supply one or more branches at desired intervals from the main pipe.

Cast iron was one of the earlier metals employed for pipe construction, and is still used to a large extent for certain work, especially for conveying water, gas, etc., below ground, as it does not easily corrode. Cast-iron pipes are also used for work above ground, in addition to wrought iron or steel and other metals; but the outer surfaces are usually painted or specially treated if the work is in exposed positions.

Steel and wrought-iron pipes are sometimes galvanised in order to resist corrosion : this applies especially to water-pipes. Copper is now extensively used for water-pipe installations, especially those of a domestic character. Pipes of special alloy, or stainless steel, are used for carrying chemical liquids, for other metals very easily corrode, or are affected by the chemicals.

For high-pressure steam installations steel pipes are used,

which usually have bolted, flanged connections. In between the flanges thin, metallic, corrugated joint-rings are placed, together with suitable jointing paste. When the bolts are tightened these rings are compressed, and ensure a steam-tight joint.

For low-pressure installations, such as used for domestic heating purposes, screwed and socketed pipe-joints are mostly employed. When used for such work the pipes are often of the drawn weldless pattern.

Other types comprise butt-welded, lap-welded, or cold-drawn weldless type.

" Butt-welded " pipes are made by a process which involves heating flat strips of the metal to a welding heat and passing them through a ring. During this stage the strips assume a circular shape and their edges " butt " together. In doing so they are welded together by the combined pressure exerted and the temperature of the metal.

The " lap-welded " system of pipe formation is somewhat similar, except that the plates are bent to a pre-determined cylindrical shape, with their edges overlapping. The plates are then heated to a welding temperature and passed through rolls, and over a template known as a " mandrel ".

The material is thus forced between the external pressure of the rolls and the internal pressure exerted by the mandrel, and the overlapping edges are therefore welded together. Pipes of 304·800 mm. or 406·400 mm. (12 inches or 16 inches) diameter may be made by this process.

" Weldless pipes ", or tubes, are formed by piercing the end of a heated bar of metal and feeding it through a die having a mandrel in the centre. The process is repeated over several dies, which, by elongating the tube, reduce the thickness of the " wall ".

" Cold-drawn, weldless " tubes are first made by the hot process just described, after which they are specially finished by drawing them—while cold—through a die and over a mandrel. Finally they are annealed. Tubes made by this process can be finished to finer limits than those obtained by any of the hot, rolled methods.

Pipes for special work, such as those used for air-conditioning plants, are sometimes formed by manually bending and riveting together plain or galvanised-iron sheets, and often their laps and joints are merely soft soldered. These pipes may be of rectangular cross-section, instead of the normal circular shape.

When used for carrying hot liquids or steam, pipes are often lagged in order to retain the heat inside them. The lagging consists of some kind of insulating material, such as asbestos yarn or other special composition, which is wrapped round the pipe in layers of suitable thickness, secured in position by wire or adhesive tape, etc. A recently discovered mineral called vermiculite has been developed and used as a basis of the compounds for lagging compositions, on account of its excellent insulating properties. Lagging of steam pipes is essential when they have to traverse a long distance, in order to prevent heat losses.

Manufacturers supply steel pipes in various grades of quality, each depending on the purpose for which they are intended. Various colour schemes have also been adopted to designate a pipe's intended use. Steam quality are painted red, and those for water are coloured blue, and so on.

A special type of screw-thread is used for pipework. This differs from the Whitworth—as used for nuts and bolts—for it is of finer, or closer, formation. (See Appendix " B " at end of this book.) A British standard has been adopted for pipe screw-threads, and that for parallel threads is tabulated in Fig. 137a. Tubes of 25·4 mm. (1 inch) diameter nominal bore and outside diameter of 1 $\frac{11}{32}$ inches have eleven threads per 25·4 mm. (inch) length.

Gas-tubes of 25·4 mm. (1 inch) nominal bore have walls No. 10 I.W.G. thick, whilst similarly bored water-tubes have walls No. 9 I.W.G. in thickness.

Note.—I.W.G. denotes Imperial Wire Gauge. For further details of gauge plate, see Vol. I, p. 87.

Gas quality tubing, in addition to being used for normal purposes, is also employed extensively as hand-railing along access platforms in boiler-houses, electric generating power-stations, etc., for which purpose it is very suitable.

Lead pipes are sometimes used for plumbing work in domestic cold-water services. They are joined merely by soft soldering the various lengths together, or by running them together, which is called wiping the joint.

Copper, brass, and other alloy pipes are chiefly made by the extrusion method, involving the use of mandrels, dies, etc., through which the material is fed while hot; and afterwards they are often finished by the cold-drawn process. By using such methods, pipes of thin and even wall thicknesses are obtained.

Fittings for pipework, bends, sockets, tees, etc., are made either by the casting process or by pressing them to shape while hot. They are made of wrought iron or mild steel, but fittings for copper or brass pipes are made of these respective materials. Having considered pipes and fittings in general, their details may now be investigated.

CAST PIPES (DETAILS) (Figs. 131 and 132)

Pipes may be made by casting them in preconstructed moulds. They can be made in iron, steel, or any of the various alloys, and may be straight, as shown in Fig. 131, with flanges at their ends, or can be curved to various radii. Cast pipes are frequently made so as to form bends of 90 degrees or more.

In order to connect together lengths of pipe, the flanges are secured by bolts and a special jointing compound is used between the joints in order to seal them efficiently. Red lead is sometimes used in paste form for this purpose, but it must *never* be used for pipes carrying water for domestic use.

The cast-iron pipe shown in Fig. 131 is the type used extensively for gas- or water-mains. A further kind has a spigot and socket (or faucet) instead of flanges for its connec-

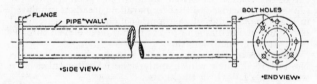

Fig. 131.—Cast-iron Pipe (with Flanged Ends).

tion (Fig. 132), and is used chiefly for gas-mains. The spigot is the end which has a small beaded lip, and the socket is the larger formation on the opposite end of the pipe, into which the spigot of the adjacent pipe fits.

Various jointing compounds are used in order to effect a seal for this kind of pipe joint, all of which finally set hard. One of the most common practices is to use molten lead as a seal. The process is as follows :—

When the spigot end of a pipe is to be connected to the socket of a pipe already laid, it is fed into the socket, and the annular space is filled with a gasket of tarred yarn for about half the depth of the socket. The yarn is then tightly rammed into position with a caulking tool and hammer.

A belt of plastic clay is then moulded all around the edge of the socket, and on the outer surface of the pipe fitted into the socket, but a hollow space is left at the socket entrance. A small pouring-hole is provided in the clay into which molten lead is poured to fill the space between the outside of the one pipe and inside the socket of the other.   The clay is then removed, and the lead—when cool—is driven tightly into the socket space by using a caulking tool.   The ring of lead seals the joint to prevent any gas escape.

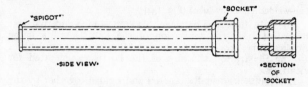

Fig. 132.—Cast-iron Pipe (with " Spigot " and " Socket " Ends).

An alternative to the molten-lead joint is the use of " lead wool ", which is made up into rope or skein form.   The lead wool is inserted into the joint (while cold) and tightly rammed into position with a caulking tool.   It is usual to insert sufficient lead wool to completely fill the socket space before final ramming is completed.

Cast-iron pipes having spigot and socketed ends are used extensively for mains and services of domestic town-gas supplies.

Most pipes cast in other metals or alloys have flanges for their joint formations.

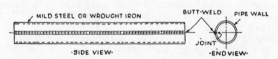

Fig. 133.—Butt-welded Tube.

Butt-welded Pipe (or Tube) (Fig. 133)

The process of manufacture of this class of pipe has been mentioned under the " general heading ".   The illustration shows an enlarged section of horizontal seam, or joint, from which will be seen (in the end view) the edges " butt " against each other.

The joint weld is also shown enlarged. Any unduly " high spots " formed during the welding are later ground off, leaving a continuous even seam along the pipe's surface.

Formerly wrought iron was used for butt-welded pipes, but it has been largely superseded of recent years by the extensive use of mild steel.

Lap-welded Pipe (or Tube) (Fig. 134)

The only difference between this kind of pipe and that just described is in the formation of the joint. As its name implies, it is " lap-welded " horizontally for its entire length. In the illustration the size of the lap is exaggerated for clearness.

Lap-joints are usually tapered and welded together by the pressure exerted as the tube is passed through the rolls and mandrel while the metal is at welding or fusing heat.

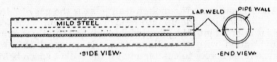

Fig. 134.—Lap-welded Tube.

During the manufacture of pipes of comparatively large diameter the metal adjacent only to the lap is heated to fusing heat. After the joint has been welded, the whole pipe is reheated and rolled true to shape, which also anneals it, and relieves any undue strains that may have developed during its partial heating for the joint-weld. Any irregularities of the lap-weld are then ground off by running it over a grinding-wheel.

Pipes exceeding 406·400 mm. or 457·200 mm. (16 inches or 18 inches) in diameter are usually made by the lap-welded method.

Cold-drawn Weldless Tube (Fig. 135)

From Fig. 135 it will be noticed that there is no longitudinal joint in the pipe. It will also be seen that the walls are of thinner formation, which results from the " cold-drawing " process. The pipe is shown, having screw-threaded ends, one of which is fitted with a socket or union (shown in dotted lines).

Pipes of small diameter are usually connected together by

sockets, if for cold-water or low-pressure installations. If, however, the pipes are for high-pressure steam services, flanges should be used, which may be either screwed on to the pipe-ends or welded to them. These remarks also apply equally well to the butt- or lap-welded types.

Pipes of all three types may also be joined together by

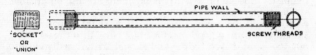

Fig. 135.—Mild Steel Cold-drawn Weldless Tube.

merely welding them, especially if they are used for carrying cold liquids at low pressures.

In order to effect a welded joint the pipe-ends should be "prepared". This consists of machining the ends to a "chamfered" or tapered formation, so that when butted together a Vee-shaped notch is formed, into which the weld is

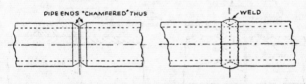

Fig. 135a.—Pipe Ends Prepared   Fig. 135b.—Joint After
       for Welding Joint.   Welding.

made and built up by depositing the weld metal into the notch so as to at least completely fill it.

Usually the welded joint is formed slightly larger than the normal pipe diameter, so that its outer surface projects beyond the pipe's surface. For pipes of large diameter several layers of " weld metal " are deposited, the effect being that each subsequent layer anneals the previous one (see Figs. 135a and 135b).

Pipe Joint Details (Screwed Socket Type) (Figs. 135 and 148)

A joint formed by a socket is simple, and one of the most common.

For cold liquid services (except for domestic water) red or white lead paste, or paint, is often smeared over the screwed pipe end prior to fitting the socket. This, in due course, " sets " and seals the joint. Graphite and oil are sometimes mixed to form a paste and applied in a similar manner. Special proprietary compounds are also obtainable.

The pipe-ends, after being cut off truly square to their axes, should be screw-threaded to a slight taper. They should also form a good comfortable " fit " into the socket— not too loose or too tight—and should be screwed well into the socket. Sometimes hemp twine is lightly lapped around the pipe's screw-threads prior to applying the joint-paste and screwing on the socket.

The joint should be completed by screwing up the socket, about half-way on to one pipe, then inserting the other pipe and screwing it into the socket. This is effected with " pipe-wrenches ", " chain-dogs ", etc., which are fully described and illustrated in Volume I, Chapter V.

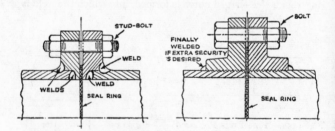

Fig. 136.—" Welded-on "
Flange Joint.

Fig. 137.—" Screwed-on "
Flange Joint.

" Welded " and " Screwed-on " Flange Joints (Figs. 136 and 137)

" Welded-on " flanges are often used for high-temperature and high-pressure pipework, and are usually electrically welded at points shown in Fig. 136.

Sometimes the inner surfaces of the flanges are " faced " or " machined ", and a joint-ring is then bolted between them to form an effective seal.

(For General Engineering Purposes). Basic Sizes. B.S. Pipe.

1	2	3	4	5	6	7	8
B.S.P. size, in.	Number of threads per inch.	Pitch, in.	Depth of thread, in.	Major diameter, in.	Effective diameter, in.	Minor diameter, in.	Cross-sectional area at bottom of thread, sq. in.
1/8	28	0·03571	0·0229	0·3830	0·3601	0·3372	0·0893
1/4	19	0·05263	0·0337	0·5180	0·4843	0·4506	0·1595
3/8	19	0·05263	0·0337	0·6560	0·6223	0·5886	0·2721
1/2	14	0·07143	0·0457	0·8250	0·7793	0·7336	0·4227
5/8	14	0·07143	0·0457	0·9020	0·8563	0·8106	0·5161
3/4	14	0·07143	0·0457	1·0410	0·9953	0·9496	0·7082
7/8	14	0·07143	0·0457	1·1890	1·1433	1·0976	0·9462
1	11	0·09091	0·0582	1·3090	1·2508	1·1926	1·117
1 1/4	11	0·09091	0·0582	1·6500	1·5918	1·5336	1·847
1 1/2	11	0·09091	0·0582	1·8820	1·8238	1·7656	2·448
1 3/4	11	0·09091	0·0582	2·1160	2·0578	1·9996	3·140
2	11	0·09091	0·0582	2·3470	2·2888	2·2306	3·908
2 1/4	11	0·09091	0·0582	2·5870	2·5288	2·4706	4·794
2 1/2	11	0·09091	0·0582	2·9600	2·9018	2·8436	6·351
2 3/4	11	0·09091	0·0582	3·2100	3·1518	3·0936	7·517
3	11	0·09091	0·0582	3·4600	3·4018	3·3436	8·780

Extracts from B.S. Number 84—1940, Table 15, British Standard Pipe Threads (Parallel), are given by permission of the British Standards Institution, 2 Park Street, London, W.1, from whom official copies can be obtained.

Note.—See Appendix " B " at end of book.

A small space should be provided between the bolt-hole faces to allow the joint-ring to be well gripped when the bolts are tightened. Fig. 137 shows a typical " screwed-on " flange-joint. This is formed by a pipe being previously screw-threaded for a sufficient length to suit the depth of the flange used.

There are two chief types of thread formation used. One is of parallel, and the other of tapered formation. The standard parallel types of screw-threads are tabulated in Fig. 137a. Sometimes, in order to ensure no possibility of leakage, the rear edge of the flange, after being screwed on to the pipe, is also welded all round.

For work of importance, especially for pipes of large diameters, the flange is also expanded by heating prior to screwing it on to the pipe, so that as it cools it contracts and grips better.

" Screwed-on " flanges may be used for pressures up to approximately 158·760 Kg. per 25·4 mm. (350 lb. per square inch), and for temperatures up to 399° C. (750° F.).

A joint-ring should always be fitted between the inner faces of the flanges, and care must be taken to tighten the flange-bolts evenly. This is best carried out by giving a few turns on each bolt-nut and working all round the flange, tightening each bolt gradually so as to distribute the pressure evenly.

Pipe or Tube Fittings (Figs. 138 to 159a inclusive)

Various fittings are used in pipe installations in order to traverse bends, form branches, corners, etc. For pipes of large diameter such fittings usually have flanges to form their connections. Pipes of comparatively small size, for conveying cold liquids, or those used for low pressures, may have screwed socket connections.

Bends may be formed merely by bending a suitable length of straight pipe to the desired curve, after which their ends are screwed-threaded and fitted with the necessary sockets. Standard bends, however, are supplied for angles of 90 degrees or greater. A typical 90-degree bend is shown in Fig. 138.

When a pipe is bent to form an angle exceeding 90 degrees it is known as a " *slow bend* "; a typical example of this is seen in Fig. 140.

A " tee-piece " is illustrated in Fig. 141. It is used for connecting three lengths of pipe, one of which is at right angles to the others. That shown is known as an " *equal tee* "-piece, because each outlet is of equal bore.

Other types are also supplied, which have the vertical

outlets of different bore from those of the horizontal outlets. They are used for " off-taking " a smaller supply of the main pipe's contents to feed another pipe at right angles.

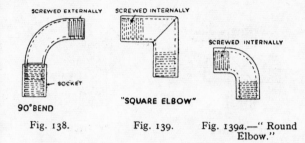

SCREWED EXTERNALLY
SCREWED INTERNALLY
SCREWED INTERNALLY
SOCKET
90°BEND
"SQUARE ELBOW"

Fig. 138. Fig. 139. Fig. 139a.—" Round Elbow."

As an example, there may be an existing pipe of 50·8 mm. (2 inches) nominal bore in an installation, to which it is desired to connect a 25·4 mm. (1-inch) bore pipe. This could

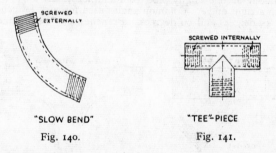

SCREWED EXTERNALLY
SCREWED INTERNALLY
"SLOW BEND"
"TEE"-PIECE

Fig. 140. Fig. 141.

be accomplished by cutting the main 50·8 mm. (2-inch) supply pipe, screw-threading the ends, and inserting a 50·8 mm. to 25·4 mm. (2-inch to 1-inch) " *unequal tee-piece* ".

A "cross-piece" is shown in Fig. 142, the purpose of which is to connect four pipes, each at right angles to an adjacent one, but all of which are in the same plane.

Fig. 143 illustrates a Y-*piece* which is used to connect three pipes of equal diameter in the formation of a letter Y.

Note.—Pipe tools, for bending, cutting, etc., are described and illustrated in Volume I.

Fig. 139 shows a " square elbow ", which has its ends screw-threaded internally. Fig. 139a depicts a " round elbow ". Either may be used to connect two pipes at right angles to each other.

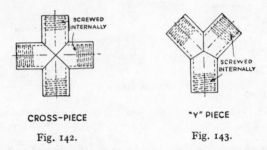

CROSS-PIECE

Fig. 142.

"Y" PIECE

Fig. 143.

The " branch-piece " shown in Fig. 144 serves the purpose of taking-off one supply pipe from another at any angle less than a right angle. Common angles used for such branches are 45 degrees and 60 degrees. Branches may be obtained

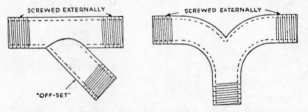

Fig. 144.—" Branch Piece."   Fig. 145.—" Twin Elbow."

either equal or unequal, as may be required, similar in principle to that described for " tee-pieces ".

Fig. 145 illustrates another fitting, known as a " twin elbow ", which may be used as an alternative to a tee-piece in some instances, and if plain sockets are fitted to its ends. When used for some liquids, or gases, the flow in a " round twin elbow " is less restricted than in a tee, owing to its gradual curved shape.

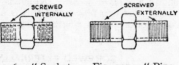

Fig. 146.—" Socket   Fig. 147.—" Pipe
      Union."   Union."

It should be noted that all the foregoing fittings with external screw-threads must have sockets attached in order to connect them up to the pipes concerned. Those

Fig. 148.—" Plain   Fig. 149.—" Re-   Fig. 150.—" Plain
   Socket."   ducing Socket."   Nipple."

with internal screw-threads are connected by merely screwing the pipes into them. For work of importance a " back-nut " may also be used to " lock " the pipe securely into position (see Fig. 155).

ENDS SCREWED EXTERNALLY

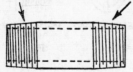

Fig. 151.—" Barrel Nipple."

A " socket union ", into which a screwed pipe may be fitted at each end, is illustrated in Fig. 146. A somewhat similar fitting, known as a " pipe union ", is shown in Fig. 147, but it is screw-threaded externally, thus requiring sockets in order to connect up pipe-lengths. Back-nuts may be employed with either of these two fittings; and lateral adjustment can also be made, depending on the threaded lengths of the pipes.

Fig. 148 shows a "*plain socket*", which is the simplest form of connection for two pipes, and this is also shown in Fig. 135 in conjunction with a length of screwed pipe.

SCREWED EXTERNALLY

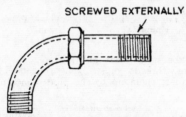

Fig. 152.—Union Bend.

The "*reducing socket*" depicted in Fig. 149 is used for connecting two pipes of unequal diameter.

The "*plain nipple*" shown in Fig. 150 is used to couple together two pipes screw-threaded internally. Two back-nuts may also be used to give extra security by locking one against the other. A "*barrel nipple*" is shown in Fig. 151.

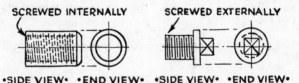

SCREWED INTERNALLY	SCREWED EXTERNALLY
•SIDE VIEW• •END VIEW•	•SIDE VIEW• •END VIEW•
Fig. 153.—A Cap.	Fig. 154.—A Plug.

In some instances the "union bend" illustrated in Fig. 152 can be used in conjunction with sockets, as an alternative to an "elbow".

In order to form a stop at one end of an open pipe, a "cap" (Fig. 153) would be employed, provided the pipe is externally screwed; but if screwed internally a "plug" (Fig. 154) would be used.

Fig. 156 shows a typical screwed flange for forming screwed-on pipe connections, and the " blank flange " (Fig. 157) is used to form a stop end on a flanged pipe.

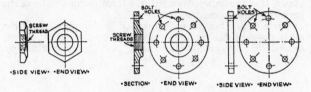

Fig. 155.—" Back-
nut."

Fig. 156.—Screwed
Flange.

Fig. 157.—Blank
Flange.

A typical double-bend, sometimes called a U bend, is shown on Fig. 158.

Fittings screw-threaded externally are termed " male ", and those screwed internally are known as " female ".

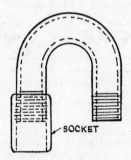

Fig. 158.—Double Bend or " U " Bend.

" Expansion Bend " (Fig. 159)

When long, straight lengths of piping are used for carrying liquids or steam at high temperatures, some means of providing for expansion must be employed.

A common component used for this purpose is the " expansion bend '' shown in Fig. 159, and one or more are installed at suitable distances along the pipe-line's length. The two extreme ends of the pipe-line are anchored down near their connections to the boiler and machinery concerned, so as to ensure that the only movement which can occur will be at the expansion bend positions.

When such a bend is to be inserted in the space left at the open ends of the straight pipe-lengths, the space should exceed slightly that of dimension " A " shown in Fig. 159,

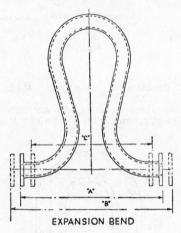

EXPANSION BEND

Fig. 159.

and should be increased to " B ". This increase provides for the bend being strained during the bolting up of its flanges, so that when, under working conditions, expansion occurs— due to the heat of the pipe's contents—dimension " B " is reduced to " C " as shown.

In reducing this dimension, the bend flanges pass through their normal or unstrained position; thus the strain on each side of the normal position is somewhat equalised, thereby reducing the liability of the bend to crack or break.

The amount of lineal expansion to be allowed for naturally depends on the temperatures involved, the length of a straight pipe-line, and the class of material used for the construction of the pipe. Such expansion figures are calculated from the data obtained when the pipe is being designed.

In addition to the bend form of expansion joint, other types are used, especially for comparatively short pipe-lines, and where expansion and contraction may occur to a lesser extent.

One form is composed of a length of copper or corrugated stainless-steel pipe, having flanges at its end. The corrugations are formed parallel to the flanges, and provide the amount of flexibility required (see Fig. 159a).

Another form comprises three " glands " or " sleeves ", which slide freely one inside the other. These glands are short lengths of pipe with a flange at one end only, usually made of brass, and accurately machined. In between the

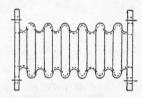

Fig. 159a.—Corrugated Expansion Joint (Bellows Type).

outer surface of one gland and the inner surface of the other some form of metallic packing is inserted to effect a " seal ".

This arrangement forms a " stuffing-box " similar to those used on steam engines where the connecting-rod enters the cylinder. When expansion occurs, one gland is merely pushed farther into the adjacent one.

Gland (Figs. 160, 160a, and 160b)

This component is used to form a seal for either hot or cold liquids. It is frequently used on steam-engine work at the ends of the cylinders to prevent steam escaping as the piston-rod moves to and fro during its strokes.

A gland is also used to prevent leakage along the spindle of a rotary water-pump. For the spindle to rotate freely there must be a slight clearance between its outer surface and the inner surface of the bearing in which it rotates.

Fig. 160 illustrates a gland used for such a pump. In the space shown some sort of packing is placed and held in position by the gland. As wear takes place, the packing can be further compressed by tightening the nuts.

Metallic packing material of soft-metal " yarn " or " lead "

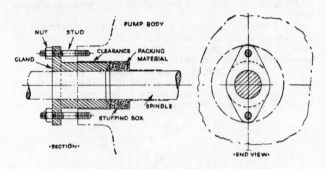

Fig. 160.—Gland attached to Water-pump Spindle.

wool is often used for this purpose, and asbestos string impregnated with graphite or saturated with tallow, grease, or thick oil is sometimes used for cold liquid services.

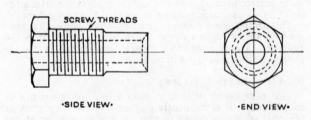

Fig. 160a.—Screw Type Gland.

Some small glands, instead of being provided with studs and nuts, are merely screw-threaded along their shanks for a short length immediately adjacent to the back of the flange, and are screwed into the bearing housing. The remaining length is also reduced in diameter and left plain. Pressure on the packing can be regulated by screwing the gland farther into its bearing (see Fig. 160a).

A further type of gland is shown in Fig. 160b. It is " plain ", and fits into a recessed nut, by means of which more pressure can be applied to the packing material as wear takes place by tightening the nut with a spanner.

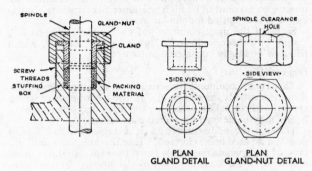

Fig. 160b.—Plain Gland Assembly.

VALVES (GENERAL)

Note.—All the valves referred to in this chapter are types used in conjunction with pipe systems for conveying gases, water, steam, etc., and are quite distinct from " poppet ", " mushroom ", or " slide-valves ", used for regulating the inlet and exhaust services to petrol, gas, or steam engine cylinders.

A valve in a pipe system is the component used for admitting or shutting off the supply of the pipe's contents. Valves vary considerably in size and construction, and the different types used amount to several hundred. Some of these in most common use are considered in this chapter.

Examples of a valve may be seen in the domestic gas-tap or water-tap, but valves vary from this size to huge types weighing several tons, such as used in conjunction with large hydro-schemes for a city's water supply. They may also be made of various metals, or alloys, each largely depending on the purpose for which it is to be employed.

G

Small valves are usually operated manually, but larger kinds may have to be power-operated.

Brass (or gun-metal) is used to a large extent for the manufacture of valves used in cold water and domestic heating systems. Cast iron and cast steel are employed for those used for many industrial purposes, cast steel being invariably used for high-pressure steam work. " Monel-metal " is often used for valve seatings and other wearing parts or fittings, especially on those used in the chemical industry, on account of its high resistance to corrosion. Stainless steel is also used for similar purposes.

Some of the most common valves are the " plug-cock ", " stop ", or " screw down ", " gate " and " reflux ", which will now be briefly considered in that order.

Plug-cock (Fig. 161)

This type, commonly referred to as a " tap " (gas tap), comprises a body, as shown in Fig. 161—both ends of which are screw-threaded for attaching the pipes, but other types of bodies may be flanged for bolted connections.

Through the body-centre, at right angles to the " line of flow ", a tapered hole is formed. Into this hole fits a similarly tapered plug, which has a hole bored through it in the position indicated, of the same diameter as the flow line in the valve-body and pipe system. The top end of the plug has a square head to which can be applied a key or spanner to operate it. For domestic use, instead of a square head, a flat handle is generally supplied (for operation between the thumb and fingers), as shown in Fig. 161a.

At the plug's lower end the diameter is reduced and a square shoulder formed, from which projects a screw-threaded end to fit a nut. A washer is fitted on the square shoulder to form a seal and also a means of retaining fixed pressure transmitted from the nut, to enable the plug to be rotated freely for its operation.

When the valve is installed in a pipe system the plug-hole cannot be seen in order to ascertain its position relative to the line of flow through it. In order to denote this, square-headed plugs have a saw-cut, or slot formed in their tops. The slot is made parallel with the plug-hole; thus when the " cock " is in the full " on " position, the slot lies parallel to the line of flow through the valve, and when the valve is turned off, the slot is at right angles to the flow line. If the plug-cock is fitted with a flat-type handle, the valve is full on when the handle lies lengthways parallel with the line of flow.

Plug-cocks of the above pattern used for domestic purposes are invariably made of brass, but for industrial purposes, brass, cast iron, or steel may be used.

This kind of valve is chiefly used for controlling gases, and must therefore be gas-tight. In order to ensure this, the plug is accurately " ground " into the cock-body, after being machined true to shape. The grinding is effected by smearing over the tapered plug surface a mixture of fine emery-powder and oil, so as to form a thin film. The plug is then inserted into the body and rotated with even pressure until an accurate " fit " is obtained.

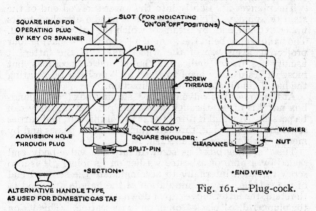

SQUARE HEAD FOR OPERATING PLUG BY KEY OR SPANNER

SLOT (FOR INDICATING "ON" OR "OFF" POSITIONS)

PLUG.

SCREW THREADS

ADMISSION HOLE THROUGH PLUG

COCK BODY

SQUARE SHOULDER

SPLIT-PIN

WASHER

NUT

CLEARANCE

•SECTION•

•END VIEW•

ALTERNATIVE HANDLE TYPE, AS USED FOR DOMESTIC GAS TAP

Fig. 161a.

Fig. 161.—Plug-cock.

When the plug is finally assembled, tallow or oil should be applied to its surface, in order to form a seal and to facilitate its rotation when in action.

When assembling the plug, the nut should be tightened just sufficiently on to the washer to allow it to rotate comfortably when reasonable pressure is applied. For important classes of work, after the nut has been finally tightened, the projecting screwed end of the plug is drilled and a split-pin applied to prevent the nut from working loose.

When the plug becomes worn, after prolonged use, it can be " re-ground ", but after grinding, care should be taken to ensure that the washer fits the square shoulder properly before replacing the nut. The shoulder must on no account project through the washer to permit it to bear on to the nut face; this is the chief point to be avoided after re-grinding.

"Globe", "Screw-down" or Stop Valves (Fig. 162, 162a and 162b)

This is depicted in its simplest form in Fig. 162. As its name implies, this valve is opened and closed by a screwing up or down of the handle. The valve comprises a body with baffles positioned inside and cast integral with it. A central vertical orifice is shown, over which fits a fibre-disc, attached to the plunger, and held securely in place by a nut.

The plunger fits tightly into the lower screwed end of the stem or spindle. This spindle has a handle attached to its upper extreme end, by means of which the valve is operated. The handle may be in the form of a " capstan "—having four projecting arms—or of the wheel type. If the latter, it usually has arrows, indicating the off and on positions, but most valves usually open to the " on " position by rotating the handle in an anti-clockwise direction.

At the top of the valve body a " stuffing-box " or " gland-box nut " is fitted, through which the plunger assembly can be passed. A gland is fitted to the top of this nut, and carries some form of packing, through which the stem passes and by means of which a seal is effected.

The " stuffing-box " is screwed into the valve-body and sealed by a fibre or asbestos washer on its joint. It is also screw-threaded internally to accommodate the screwed end of the spindle. By manipulation of the handle attached to the stem, the latter moves up or down, thus lifting or lowering the plunger-disc " clack " off or on to its seating. This action thus opens or closes the orifice and regulates the flow.

The type of valve illustrated is commonly used for domestic and industrial hot-water systems of low pressure, but improved patterns are used for other purposes. These may have renewable seatings of special alloy material, or alloy plungers instead of that fitted with a fibre disc-washer shown in the illustration.

Larger types also have bolted connections for the stuffing-box, and gland assemblies, and may have square-threaded spindles and handle-wheels of large diameter. Although that shown in the illustration has its ends internally screw-threaded, larger sizes usually have drilled flanges for bolted connections.

Valves of the " globe " stop-type are sometimes equipped with a solid stainless-steel ball fitted into a cup-shaped

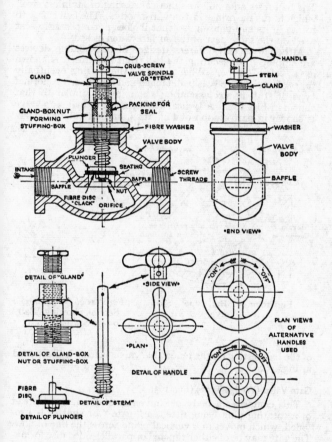

Fig. 162.—" Globe ", " Screw-down " or Stop Valve.

housing at the spindle-base, instead of a disc-type "clack". The ball rests on a hollow spherical seating of stainless steel, which forms the orifice in the valve body. The ball is free to rotate in its cup-housing, so that it does not repeatedly seat itself on the same part of the surface when closed.

Although several different designs of ball-holding devices are employed for securing the ball, that illustrated is known as a "claw" type. When wear of the seating eventually takes place, it can be easily detached and renewed. A normal type of stuffing-box assembly is employed, similar to that shown in Fig. 162. A typical arrangement of ball-stop valve is shown in part section of Fig. 162a, and an enlarged view

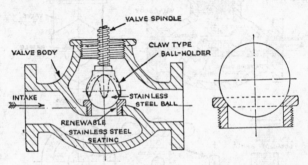

Fig. 162a.—" Ball-type " Stop Valve.

Fig. 162b. — Enlarged Section Showing "Ball" on its Seating.

of the ball resting on the renewable valve-seating is illustrated in Fig. 162b.

Gate Valve (Wedge Type) (Fig. 163)

This comprises a body of conventional form, but instead of a rotating plug being fitted, a "gate" or shutter is provided, which moves in a vertical plane across the line of flow. The gate may be of either tapered or parallel-sided disc formation. That shown in Fig. 163 has a tapered or wedge-shaped gate, which is accurately machined and made to fit the tapered seatings of the valve-body.

As will be seen from the illustration, a sediment chamber is formed in the valve body immediately below the gate, and is fitted with a drain-plug. This forms a means of clearing away any accumulated dirt or sediment, etc., which may be deposited from the fluid being dealt with.

At the wedge-gate top a nut is fitted into which the operating spindle is placed. This nut is located in a casing projection attached to the gate, so that as the spindle is

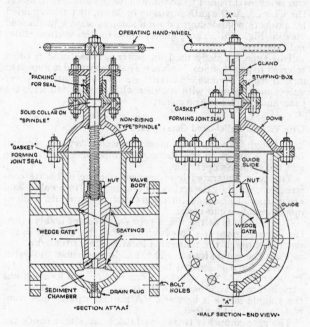

Fig. 163.—Gate Valve ("Wedge" Type).

rotated by the hand-wheel, the nut, together with the gate, is raised or lowered, respectively, thus opening or closing the valve. At the position shown, a solid collar is formed on the spindle, which, although free to rotate, cannot move vertically, and it therefore provides a means of locating and maintaining the spindle in position.

High-class valves have renewable gun-metal bushes in

which the spindle-collar rotates. The spindle-collar housing is in two pieces, the top piece also forming a stuffing-box to provide a seal. Suitable packing is fitted in the stuffing-box and retained in position by the gland.

The top end of the spindle is reduced in diameter, fitted with a square shoulder for the hand-wheel, and the extreme end is screw-threaded to accommodate the nut and to secure the wheel. As the gate moves up or down, its path is guided by projection guide-lugs on each side, as shown in the end view of Fig. 163. These guides move on the vertical slides indicated.

This type is chiefly used for water services, and is often referred to as a " sluice " valve. That illustrated is known as a non-rising spindle pattern. As an alternative, other valves may be used with spindles which rise or fall with the gate, and which have no collar.

Gate Valve (Parallel-faced Gate) (Fig. 164)

Although closely resembling the wedge-type in general form, this differs in the shape and construction of its gate and the spindle's operation.

The type illustrated is of somewhat more elaborate construction, for its gate and body seatings are renewable, and are of special heat-and-corrosion-resisting materials, such as monel metal or gun-metal.

The spindle is of the rising type—*i.e.* it rises bodily when the valve is opened. This is effected by the screwed length passing through the renewable locating nut, situated at the top of the guide-frame. The hand-wheel does not rise, however, for it is secured to the locating nut by means of a grub-screw. As the wheel is rotated, so is the locating nut attached to it, and, owing to the latter being screw-threaded, the spindle inside it is raised. A normal stuffing-box complete with gland is fitted.

The gate comprises two sleeved discs, one sleeve inside the other. In the centre of the inner sleeve a coil-compression spring is placed, which exerts pressure on to the body seating-rings, thus maintaining an effective seal. The renewable seatings are either pressed firmly into position or secured by screws.

In some forms of valve construction the whole of the sleeved disc is formed of special alloy, instead of having renewable disc-seatings. The discs are fitted into a housing, to which is attached a lug, and into the lug fits the lower end of the spindle, which is secured in position by a nut similar to that shown in Fig. 163.   The disc slides on vertical guides as indicated.

The valve shown in Fig. 164 is suitable for high-pressure steam installations, and is known as a rising-spindle pattern,

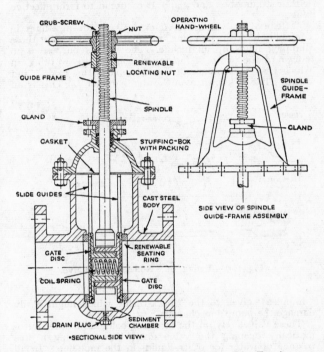

GRUB-SCREW
NUT
OPERATING HAND-WHEEL
RENEWABLE LOCATING NUT
GUIDE FRAME
SPINDLE GUIDE-FRAME
GLAND
SPINDLE
GLAND
GASKET
STUFFING-BOX WITH PACKING
SLIDE GUIDES
CAST STEEL BODY
SIDE VIEW OF SPINDLE GUIDE-FRAME ASSEMBLY
GATE DISC
RENEWABLE SEATING RING
COIL SPRING
GATE DISC
DRAIN PLUG
SEDIMENT CHAMBER
•SECTIONAL SIDE VIEW•

Fig. 164.—Gate Valve (Parallel Sliding Disc Type).

but some are made with non-rising spindles similar to that shown in Fig. 163, and with hand-wheels which are firmly attached to rising spindles.

Reflux or " Non-return " Valve (Fig. 165)

A reflux valve is the " flap " type, and operates in one direction only.   It comprises a chamber as shown with a cover-plate on top. Through the body passes a horizontal spindle, or hinge-pin, on which is mounted a door, or flap suspended freely. These are mounted in lugs formed on the outside walls of the valve-body chamber. The spindle is fitted with a stuffing-box and gland at each end to form effective seals.

"Reflux" valves are used extensively for pipe-lines in conjunction with pumping installations, especially those pumping fluids up an incline. The valve's purpose is to safeguard the pump, if for any reason it stops working, in which case the column of liquid would "run back" and create what is known as a "water hammer". This is an

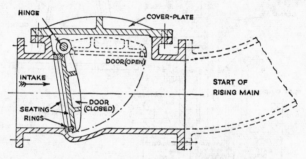

Fig. 165.—Reflux, or " Non-return " Valve.

"impulse" given to the "back-rush" which might easily damage the pump's mechanism.

These valves rely on the incoming column of water automatically opening the valve door, thus allowing a free passage of water (or other liquid) in the pipe-line. In all pumping plants the water is delivered under pressure to the pipe mains, and it is this pressure which opens the valve door. The valve illustrated is of elementary design, of the single-door pattern, but others are made having multiple doors.

Fig. 165 shows renewable seating-rings in both the valve-body and the door. These rings may be of gun-metal, monel metal, or stainless steel, depending on the nature of the job.

Close attention should be paid to the packing used in the stuffing-box, for it should not be of too hard a material, which in due course may damage the spindle. Furthermore, it may cause unnecessary " binding ", thus increasing the force required to open the valve door.

In cheap forms of construction the bearings may be plain gun-metal bushes, fitted with grease lubricators. These should receive frequent inspection and be kept well greased. Reflux valves of more elaborate construction are sometimes fitted with a " by-pass " branch pipe complete with a small regulating valve for " priming " purposes.

Should a reflux valve be installed in a pipe-line pumping " river-water ", which may contain grit or other foreign bodies in addition to the suction pipe being fitted with a strainer, the valve body should have a sediment chamber with drain-plug attached, in order to remove periodically any accumulated sediment which might otherwise clog the door base and prevent it from closing when required.

SAFETY-VALVES (GENERAL)

In connection with steam installations, especially boilers, some precaution must be taken to safeguard pressures from rising to an unsafe degree. For this purpose a component known as a " safety-valve " is used.

There are several forms, but in general each incorporates a " plug "-type valve, retained in the seating of a chamber installed in the boiler-shell, and connected by a direct passage to inside the steam-chest. The valve is retained in position on its seatings against the pressure of steam inside the boiler either by a weighted lever, series of weights, or a spring.

Should the pressure rise above a pre-determined amount, the force exerted lifts the valve, releases steam to the atmosphere, and prevents the boiler from bursting. On " fire-tube " types of boilers what is termed a " fusible " plug is incorporated in a convenient part of the boiler-shell, known as the " crown-plate " immediately over the fire-box.

The detailed construction of some common types of safety-valves may now be considered.

Safety-valve (Lever Type) (Fig. 166)

On reference being made to the illustration (Fig. 166), it will be seen that this component consists of a hollow, cylindrical-shaped body into which is screwed a renewable " seating "—also of hollow cylindrical form. Mounted on this is a " plug-shaped " valve freely suspended from a lever.

The lever is positioned directly over the valve, and is hinged (or pivoted) where shown. Towards the lever's opposite end, and at a pre-determined distance from the valve, is a cast-iron balance weight which is secured to the lever by a set-screw, and by means of which the weight can be slid along and fixed in any position to give a certain leverage, thus providing for the valve to open at a pre-determined boiler pressure.

By the principle of " moments " or " leverage ", the closer the weight is to the valve, the lower will be the steam pressure required to open it, and vice versa.

Note.—This principle is fully explained in any elementary book on " Applied Mechanics ", if not already understood by the reader.

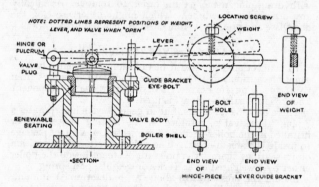

Fig. 166.—Safety-valve (Lever Type).

A guide-bracket is fitted to maintain the lever in alignment. The valve-body, seating, and plug are all made of gun-metal; the lever, brackets, etc., are made of mild steel, and the weight is of cast-iron construction. This pattern of valve is used chiefly for stationary boilers.

Safety-valve (Dead-weight Pattern) (Fig. 167)

This is of simple construction, and reliable, but is unsuitable for high pressures. It is mostly used for low-pressure stationary boilers, such as domestic heating installations. The valve has an inverted " dome "-shaped plug, from which protrudes a short stem or spindle. The plug is freely mounted at the top of a tubular-shaped seating, that also forms the body and is made integral with the casing.

The plug-stem projects through the fixing gland.   To the latter is attached a hollow cylinder, having a ledge formation at its base, on which cast-iron weights of annular construction are placed.   The weights thus retain the plug in position on the seating against the internal steam pressure exerted by the boiler.

Small arrows indicate the path taken by the steam, which, on reaching a pre-determined pressure, lifts the plug, thereby opening the seating orifice, and releasing the steam to the

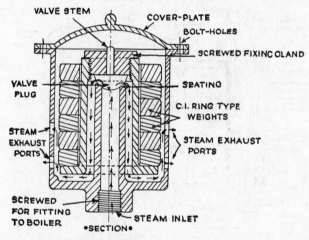

VALVE STEM

COVER-PLATE

BOLT-HOLES

SCREWED FIXING GLAND

VALVE PLUG

SEATING

C.I. RING TYPE WEIGHTS

STEAM EXHAUST PORTS

STEAM EXHAUST PORTS

SCREWED FOR FITTING TO BOILER

STEAM INLET

•SECTION•

Fig. 167.—Safety-valve (Dead-weight Type).

" exhaust-ports ".   By varying the number of weights used, the valve can be arranged to open or release at various given pressures.

Safety-valve (Spring Pattern) (Fig. 168)

When required for boilers of a portable nature, such as those of locomotive engines, cranes, etc., the " spring "-type valve is more satisfactory, as it can withstand vibration. It has also several additional refinements, and can be supplied with renewable seatings recessed into the body.

It will be seen from the illustration that the plug is of

orthodox design, but its position is retained in the seating by pressure exerted from the helical coil spring. This pressure can be regulated by means of the screwed adjustable sleeve, which is also secured in any desired position by the lock-nut. Springs of square cross-sectional formation are often employed as alternatives to that of the circular cross-sectional shape illustrated.

Once the gland and lock-nut have been finally set to give a specified release pressure on the spring, the cover can be

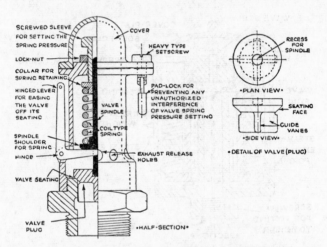

Fig. 168.—Safety-valve (Enclosed Spring Type).

secured by the padlock shown, thus preventing interference with the setting. A hinged lever is also attached to the lower casing, whereby the valve-plug may be eased occasionally from its seating in order to test it for sticking.

The spring is held in position between the solid shoulder on the lower part of the spindle and the sliding collar immediately adjacent to the screwed sleeve. When the valve-plug is raised from its seating, the steam escapes via the exhaust holes spaced around the casing perimeter.

This type of safety-valve is made entirely of gun-metal—except, of course, the spring, which is steel.

Fusible Plug (Fig. 169)

The fusible plug briefly referred to under the general heading is in a certain way another form of safety device. It

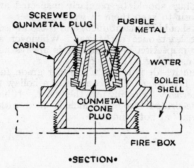

•SECTION•

Fig. 169.—Fusible Plug (for a Boiler).

comprises a gun-metal screwed sleeve (or gland), into which is screwed another smaller sleeve. In the centre of the latter

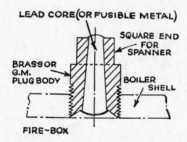

Fig. 169a.—Fusible Plug (Alternative Type).

is a hollow gun-metal cone. Between the outside of the cone and the inside of the inner sleeve, some fusible metal (usually lead) or a mixture of tin and lead, is used as filling.

When the water-level falls below the boiler crown-plate

level, the subsequent rise in temperature of the plate melts the lead and allows the cone to fall out. Through the hole thus left, wet steam escapes on to the fire below and damps it out.

Fusible plugs should be regularly inspected and cleaned of any deposit to keep them in working order. A stock of spare plugs should be maintained, and those in use should be replaced at least once each year. Whenever a boiler is drained for inspection or repairs, it is always advisable to replace the used plug by a new one.

An alternative design, and a cheaper grade fusible plug, is shown in Fig. 169a. This consists of a hollow brass plug, screwed externally for fitting into the boiler. It has a central tapered hole drilled through, which is filled with lead and " burred over " at both ends.

CHAPTER X

SPRINGS—COMPRESSION, TENSION, TORSION AND LAMINATED, ETC. (GENERAL)

A SPRING is a component used for many purposes in all classes of engineering work. It is of an elastic or flexible nature, and may be used for providing resilience to some adjacent component, or solely for exerting pressure. A spring may also be employed to give a quick return motion to some component brought into a certain position by other means, or it can be utilised solely as a buffer, to diminish shock. There are several forms in common use, each of which serves some specific purpose.

Springs are usually made from a special quality of metal known as " spring "-steel, which is of a durable, hard character. In addition to steel, bronze is occasionally employed for special purposes, and rubber is sometimes used, especially when employed as a " buffer " to " damp down " or eliminate vibration. Furthermore, steel in itself possesses elasticity to a certain degree; this property is made use of in a modern type of spring design known as the " torsion-bar " principle.

Some previous chapters contain illustrations of components in which springs appear as parts thereof, and from which their general applications will no doubt have been noted.

Consideration may now be given to detailed formations of some common types of springs.

Helical Compression Spring (Figs. 170 and 171)

When steel of rod formation is coiled into the shape of a " helix ", and a space is left between the coils, the result is as shown in Figs. 170 and 171. Such formations, if made of " spring "-quality steel, form " compression " springs. This means that if they are compressed in the direction of the arrows, they " re-act ", or attain a resilient property, commonly termed " elasticity ".

This elasticity is made use of for many purposes in engineering, such as for closing quickly the valves of internal-combustion engines after their having been opened by mechanical

H   209

means. A further example of their application has been seen in the steam safety-valve shown in Fig. 168, whereby the spring's energy is employed for retaining the valve-plug in its closed position.

Such springs may be formed from either round or square

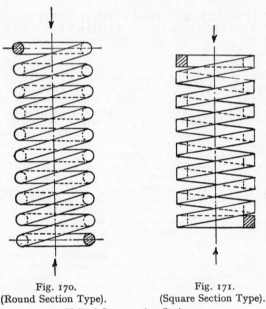

Fig. 170.
(Round Section Type).

Fig. 171.
(Square Section Type).

Helical Compression Springs.

section materials, depending on the nature of the job. Square-section steel is often employed for heavy duty work.

When retained in store, and therefore not in use, springs should never be kept " loaded ", or their full elastic properties may diminish.

Helical Tension Spring (Fig. 172)

Here it will be seen, from the illustration, that the coiled formation somewhat resembles that of Figs. 170 and 171, except that the individual "coils" are touching each other. The action of a "tension" spring is the reverse of those just considered. It also has a hook at each end of its formation in order to attach it to other components.

The application of a tension spring is effected by "pulling" it lengthways; in so doing, energy is expended, which it reclaims by a tendency to revert to its original shape. This tendency is therefore utilised when two other components—to which the spring is attached—are desired to be retained by a force tending to "pull" them together.

An elementary example of this is seen in a domestic "spring balance" (weighing machine) by means of which—as the spring is extended alongside a graduated scale—the equivalent load is read off. When the load is released, the spring reverts to its original closed-up position.

A further practical example of a tension spring's application may be seen in connection with brake-rod pedals for motor-cars and motor-cycles, and in cases where employed to maintain the "brake-shoe" in the "*off*" position until pressure of the foot is applied to put "*on*" the brake.

Fig. 172.— Helical Tension Spring.

Tension springs are not perhaps used so extensively as those of the compression type in general engineering.

HELICAL CONE SPRING (VOLUTE TYPE) (Fig. 173)

HELICAL CONE SPRING "VOLUTE" (COMPRESSION TYPE)

Fig. 173.

If a flat strip of spring-steel is coiled to "volute" formation, so as to form a cone—illustrated in Fig. 173—when fully compressed each individual coil recedes into its adjacent one. A spring of this pattern therefore requires less space longitudinally than a compression spring of orthodox parallel helical design when fully compressed. It is therefore used as an alternative, or in special instances, in place of a compression spring.

LAMINATED PLATE SPRING (Fig. 174)

This consists of a number of partially curved strips of steel, usually called "leaves". All are of equal width and thickness, but of unequal length, as shown in Fig. 174. The leaves are secured by clamping them together at the centre. The uppermost "leaf" usually has its ends bent to form holes into which fit "shackle-pins". For work of importance

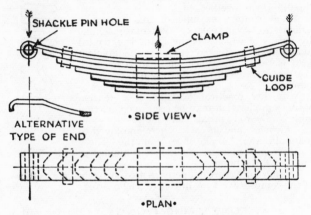

Fig. 174.—Laminated Plate Spring.

these ends are fitted with gun-metal, or other types of bushes, which, owing to the swivelling motion developed by the shackle-links, are in constant motion.

The principle on which such springs operate is that, as pressure is exerted in the direction of the arrows and in the centre, there is a tendency for the leaves to straighten. This provides elasticity or flexibility, but in so doing the end portion of each leaf slides along the surface of its adjacent one. It is therefore essential to provide them with some form of lubrication, for which grease is employed.

Under working conditions, when pressure is exerted on the spring, and during the straightening tendency, the distance between the two shackle pin-holes is increased. Provision is made for this by arranging the shackle ends free to move on their pivots.

Laminated plate springs, of the pattern illustrated, are widely used in automobile construction, as main chassis suspension springs. Those of similar general construction, but with the alternative top leaf end design (as shown), are used universally for railway rolling-stock and locomotives. The ends of the top leaf, instead of being provided with shackle-pin holes, have guides fitted to the chassis, in which the spring-ends are free to slide as pressure is exerted from the axles.

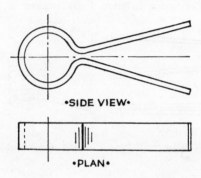

•SIDE VIEW•

•PLAN•

Fig. 175.—" Lock "-type Spring.

" LOCK "-TYPE SPRING (Fig. 175)

The spring shown in the illustration is used for operating the mechanism of " rim-type " or " mortice " door-locks and catches. When a door-knob handle is turned by hand, it is this type of spring which is used to return the catch automatically when the hand pressure is released. This kind of spring is also used for other light classes of mechanisms.

HAIR-PIN SPRING (Fig. 176)

Another class of spring used for light engineering and electrical engineering work is the " hair-pin ", which consists of one circular coil from the ends of which project two straight arms. An elementary example of its application can be seen in the domestic " safety-pin "

" TORSION-COIL " SPRING (Fig. 177)

A more advanced application of the principle of the " hairpin " spring will be seen in the torsion-coil pattern illustrated in Fig. 177. This consists of multiple coils of round steel wire, from the first and last coils of which the wire is projected to form " arms ".

The straight arm is rigidly fixed in position, and the other arm is fitted around the object to which a rotating motion of a rebounding character is required. Before being fitted, however, the spring is strained (by tending to uncoil it).

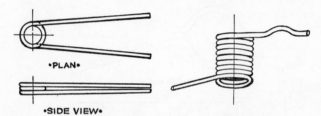

•PLAN•

•SIDE VIEW•

Fig. 176.—" Hair-pin " Type   Fig. 177.—Torsion Coil
Spring.   Spring.

In so doing, its inertia is developed, and thus transmitted to the object in question.

This type of spring, in addition to numerous other applications, is used extensively for the roller-type handle-bar brakes of pedal cycles. By this means the brakes are retained in the " off " position until hand pressure is applied to them, and when the hand pressure is released the brakes are also released. The spring action is thus developed by " torsion " or " twisting " the series of coils.

" TORSION-BAR " SPRING (Figs. 178 and 179)

As previously mentioned (under the general heading of this chapter), steel in itself possesses elasticity to a certain extent. Let it therefore be assumed that a length of round spring steel bar is rigidly secured at one end in a vice, with the other end free.

If the free end is now firmly gripped and *twisted* axially, then on releasing the pressure the bar will revert to its original shape (providing its " elastic limit " has not been exceeded).

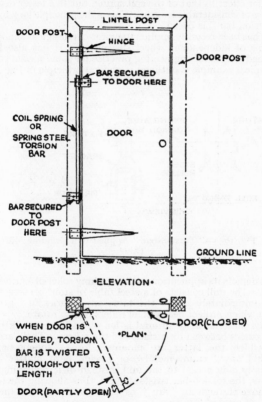

Fig. 178.—Coil Spring, or Steel " Torsion-bar " Applied to a Door.

No doubt most readers will have seen garden gates, or doors fitted with a length of coil-steel spring (one end of which is attached to the door, and the other end to the post), as a means of automatically closing the gate (see Fig. 178).

Assuming the spring is replaced by a suitable length of straight, round spring-steel bar, the bar would then have a similar effect to that of the coil spring, but to a lesser degree, unless of considerable length. This is the principle on which a " torsion bar " is based.

It has been recently applied to motor-car design as a modern means of independent wheel suspension. It has also been applied to general engineering practice for some special cases. A typical example is outlined in general principle in Fig. 179.

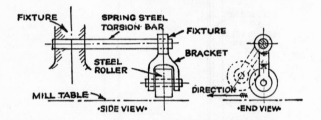

Fig. 179.—" Torsion-bar " Applied to a Grinding Mill Table.

This depicts its application to the crushing roller of a grinding-mill. The mill consists of a steel table of stout construction, and immediately above the table are a series of " arms " from which project heavy steel rollers free to rotate.

The material to be ground is fed on to the rotating table and passes between its surface and the rollers. The " arms " on which the latter are mounted form " torsion-bars ". Should any " tramp-metal " or foreign hard matter accidentally gain access to the mill, instead of it damaging the rollers, the torsion-bar twists slightly, thus allowing the roller to move through an " arc ", as shown in the dotted lines of the end view of Fig. 179.

VOLUTE COIL SPRING (Fig. 180)

If a strip of steel has one end fixed to a point of a round steel bar and is then coiled around the bar so that the radius of the strip is constantly increasing, a formation of spring known as " volute " is developed, as shown in the illustration of Fig. 180.

This type of spring forms the basis of motive power for mechanisms such as clocks, watches, gramophones, etc. The " hair-spring " of a pocket or wrist-watch is also of

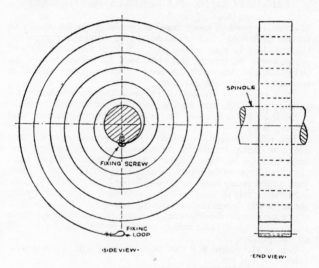

Fig. 180.—Volute Flat Coil Spring
(or " Clock "-type).

similar formation. It is commonly called a " clock-type " spring or " flat spiral ", and is used for light classes of engineering, especially for recording-instrument manufacture.

PART 2

CHAPTER XI

ENGINEERING MATERIALS (GENERAL)

MATERIALS used in mechanical engineering consist chiefly of metals and alloys, which have almost completely replaced timber—largely used in the past. Except for some parts of agricultural machinery and that used for certain chemicals (which might otherwise adversely affect metals), timber is now used only in isolated cases.

India-rubber is employed for some purposes—mainly for fittings, packings, and washers, or in order to form "seals".

Leather is also used for washers, pump-plungers and driving-belts.

Recently various " plastics " have been developed, and are now being employed for fittings such as brackets and lever-handles on many light classes of work. They have the advantage of being easily moulded into desired shapes, but, whilst being hard, some are liable to be brittle.

Since metals of various types and their alloys are by far the most widely used materials with which the student will be concerned, brief descriptions of some of the most common will now be given, and mention made of their chief uses and characteristics.

One of the oldest is " cast iron ", which will be dealt with first.

CAST IRON

This is made from iron-ore by " smelting " it in a " kiln " or chamber, called a " blast-furnace ".

Here the raw ore is mixed with some " flux " (such as lime-stone, or clay) and heated to a molten state, by using coke together with a blast of air. During this smelting process, and whilst the ore is being reduced to iron, the latter absorbs carbon from the coke, which renders it more fluid and permits the iron to settle at the furnace base, whence it is " run-off " into sand moulds, or a " pig-casting " machine, and on cooling forms blocks called " pigs ".

Note.—OXYGEN is in many cases NOW USED INSTEAD OF AIR, from which higher temperatures are obtained.

These " pigs " are slabs of " iron " in its crude form, which in due course undergo other treatment to render them suitable for the purposes desired.

In their "crude" state the pigs either pass to the foundry for conversion into "cast iron", or are used for the making of wrought iron, steel, etc.

For the manufacture of cast iron, the "pigs" are re-melted at the foundry in a smaller type of furnace—called a "cupola". Here the "pigs" are broken up and packed into the cupola between alternate layers of coke. The latter is ignited and supplied with a continuous air-blast which enters the cupola near the base and is directed upwards through the contents. The oxygen from the air-blast burns the coke, raising the temperature of the mixture and melting the iron. In so doing, the iron absorbs small quantities of impurities, such as sulphur from the coke. By this time the iron may contain from 2 to 5 per cent. of carbon, as well as small amounts of oxides, silicates, manganese, sulphur, phosphorus, etc.

In order to reduce the carbon content, it is usual to add to the "mix", during the re-melting process, a certain amount of iron lower in carbon, such as "scrap" wrought-iron, or "scrap" mild-steel.

For the manufacture of special grades of cast iron, small quantities of other ingredients are sometimes added to the mix, such as nickel, chromium, molybdenum, silicon, etc., while it is in its molten state.

Note.—The quality of cast iron finally produced also depends to a certain extent on the origin from which the raw iron-ore was obtained for manufacturing the "pigs", as the chemical contents of iron ores from various parts of the country naturally vary to some degree.

When the molten metal in the cupola is ready for use it is run-off into a tilting-type refractory-lined "ladle", in which it is conveyed and poured into a previously prepared "mould"—made to the shape of the desired "casting".

The mould is composed of damp sand, mixed with coal dust or loam, and is shaped from a previously constructed timber, metal or plaster pattern.

Cast iron, in common with all metals, has a crystalline structure, and is fairly hard, but brittle, because the carbon in excess of 1 per cent. forms graphite flakes which break the continuity of the crystal structure.

Note.—See Appendix "A" at end of book.

It is used for making special-shaped objects which would otherwise be difficult to construct by "forging" or other means.

Cast iron is strong in "compression" but weak in "tension". It is therefore used for making bases for machinery, stands, engine bed-plates, frameworks for machines, brackets, pedestal-bodies, bearing-housings, gear-wheels, pulleys, intricate casings for machinery, engine cylinders, domestic utensils, fire-grates, and architectural fittings of an ornamental nature, or anything in which tensile stress is not involved.

Although the ultimate "tensile" stress of cast iron may be between 5,080 Kg. and 11,176 Kg. per 25·4 mm² (5 and 11 tons per square inch), its ultimate "crushing" stress is in the region of 40,640 Kg. to 45,720 Kg. per 25·4 mm² (40 to 45 tons per square inch).

Grey cast iron can be easily "machined", and can now be "welded" by taking special precautions. It is more capable of resistance to atmospheric corrosion than mild steel. See Appendix " A " at the end of this chapter.

"Iron" is the basis of the majority of materials used in engineering, either by itself or "alloyed" with other metals, according to each particular purpose for which they are required. It is the basis of " steel ", " semi-steel ", " wrought iron ", etc.

Malleable Cast Iron is produced by heating a special kind (white cast iron) of iron " casting " in some oxidising material for several days and retaining it at a certain temperature. The material used is " hæmatite ", which absorbs from the iron a certain amount of carbon and changes the remainder to graphite in " rosette " form, thus rendering it less brittle, increasing its tenacity, and making it more ductile. This " absorption " is more prominent on the outer surfaces of a casting, on account of their closer proximity to the hæmatite.

Semi-Steel is the term used for a casting which is made from a mixture of "pig-iron" and wrought iron (or scrap mild steel) by re-melting together in the cupola.

Such castings are somewhat less brittle than ordinary cast iron, and are thus more ductile, owing to the resulting product containing less carbon.

WROUGHT IRON (OR "WROT" IRON)

Wrought iron is an almost carbon-free iron made from " pig-iron ". It is of a " fibrous " structure formation, and the carbon from the " pig " is considerably reduced—if not entirely eliminated—by a process known as " puddling ". This consists of breaking up the " pigs " (which are themselves a selected class known as " white-pigs "—preferably containing not more than 2 or 2½ per cent. carbon), and mixing them with iron oxide, in a special kind of chamber, called a " puddling-furnace ".

This furnace is supplied with an air-blast, and the mixture is periodically agitated, the object being to " burn off " all, or as much as possible, of the carbon content. The resulting product is a soft "pasty" mass—called a "bloom". Whilst still hot it is subjected to a constant hammering or squeezing process to remove oxide slag. The process is repeated several times, each of which tends to further reduce the carbon content, until it is practically eliminated. This treatment gives the material a " fibrous " nature, the fibres being slag. Finally, the product passes to the rolling mills, where it is "rolled" into commercial sections and plates, etc.

The final quality of wrought iron depends on the amount of puddling, hammering, squeezing, and rolling to which it has been subjected during its manufacture.

Good-quality wrought iron can be bent (while cold) to small radii without fracturing or showing signs of fracture.

It has the advantage of being less liable to atmospheric corrosion or " rusting " than mild steel, and has a tensile strength of 20,320 to 24,384 Kg. per 25·4 mm.² (20 to 24 tons per square inch).

Its chief uses are for architectural fittings, outdoor ornamentation of buildings, the making of rivets, boiler-plates, forgings, etc.

STEEL (GENERAL)

On account of there being so many varieties of this material, the term " steel " is somewhat vague. The term applies chiefly to a product of iron—a certain amount of carbon, and other ingredients. To a certain extent the quality is governed by its carbon content.

Steel is produced by melting cast iron (" pigs ") and refining it to remove some of the carbon and other impurities. The hardness of steel also depends mainly on its carbon content.

Unlike wrought iron, steel is easily rusted. Qualities of steel which contain only relatively small quantities of carbon can be forged and welded, but cannot be " cast ". Steel containing from 0·6 per cent. up to approximately 1·2 per cent. is, however, suitable for casting or for making " tools ", etc.

The ultimate tensile strength of steel may vary between 28,448 Kg. and 254,000 Kg. per 25·4 mm.² (28 and 250 tons per square inch), depending on its carbon content, heat treatment, mechanical treatment, and, or, alloy additions; the higher tensile stresses being those of piano wire, etc.

Steel is used for multiple purposes, each depending on its quality. It is used for shafts, gears, castings, springs, and all classes of tools. All steels can be heat-treated in many ways for such purposes as to increase their hardness through out, or to increase the surface hardness.

MILD STEEL (OR STRUCTURAL STEEL)

One of the chief differences between mild steel and wrought iron is that the former has a higher carbon content—usually up to 0·30 per cent. Mild steel also rusts easily and is therefore not so durable.

It is equally strong in tension or compression, and has an ultimate tensile stress of 28,448 Kg. to 32,482 Kg. per 25·4 mm.^{2} (28 to 32 tons per square inch). On account of its relative cheapness as compared with wrought iron, it has largely replaced the latter, is used extensively for making boiler-plates, sheet-metal work, and is rolled into sections for structural purposes, for which it is employed extensively. It is also used for frames of machinery, and, as it can be welded, is now often used for " built-up " sections, instead of casting them in iron.

ALLOY STEEL

This is the term applied when steel is mixed with one or more " alloys ", such as nickel, chromium, tungsten, molybdenum, vanadium, manganese, cobalt, etc.

STAINLESS STEEL

This is a product formed by mixing steel with up to about 20 per cent. chromium, which gives it the property of resisting corrosion permanently.

It is used extensively for chemical and other machinery, on account of its corrosion-resisting properties, and is also used for cutlery and domestic articles. Stainless steel is now used for motor car bumpers, and windscreen frames, fittings, etc.

CAST STEEL

This is a special " mix " containing certain amounts of the following: carbon, silicon, sulphur, phosphorus, and manganese.

According to variation of the mixing of the above material, the resulting product is relatively " soft " or " hard ". Cast steel used for brackets, etc., or heavy industrial " castings ", is rough, durable, and comparatively hard. That used for tool-making is much harder, but is liable to be brittle. Cast steel is usually made by what are termed the "electric furnace" or "crucible" processes, which differ from the method of manufacture for "structural" or "mild steel". It is also unsuitable for "forging", and cannot be easily "welded".

Steel " castings " are usually " annealed " prior to use— *i.e.* they are rendered softer by heat treatment.

MANGANESE STEEL

When the manganese content of steel is increased in the region of 12 to 14 per cent., the product attains high resistance to wear and becomes hard and durable.

Messrs. Hadfields, Ltd., of Sheffield, were the originators and patentees of the product known as " manganese steel ", but it is now also made by other firms. Owing to its hard-wearing properties, it is used extensively for railway and tramway " points " and " crossings ", also for the wearing surfaces of crushing and grinding machinery. Owing to its hardness, the material cannot be " drilled " by normal methods, therefore holes formed in it are usually of the " cored " type (*i.e.* they are formed during the casting of the metal). It is also too hard for machining or filing, so any surface treatment is usually done by " grinding ".

CARBON STEEL (TOOL)

This is a special quality, containing a higher carbon content, and is used for making small tools (drills, taps, dies, saws, etc.). It requires " quenching " in water during its " hardening " process.

SELF- (OR AIR-) HARDENING TOOL STEEL

This is an alloy steel which after heating, during the hardening process, instead of then " quenching ", attains its degree of hardness by " cooling off " slowly in the air.

HIGH-SPEED TOOL STEEL

This is a special class containing high tungsten content, plus other alloys that attains its maximum hardness after heating to a very high degree—almost to its " fusing " temperature—and then quenching in an air blast, followed by a " secondary hardening " heat treatment. It is now used extensively for " cutting tools " in connection with lathe-work, etc.

HEAT-RESISTING STEEL

This is a particular grade, containing pre-determined amounts of chromium and other alloys whose combination forms a crust on the steel's surface (when subjected to heat) which resists the oxidisation caused by heating in an atmosphere containing oxygen.

Note.—All the foregoing materials are termed " ferrous " metals (*i.e.* they contain " iron " in some form or other). Consideration will now be given to some of the properties of " NON-FERROUS " metals and alloys, etc.

NON-FERROUS METALS

Copper. This metal is obtained from copper ore by smelting and refining it. Its colour is of golden-brown when in a finished commercial state.

It resists corrosion well, can be " cast " and " forged " or " rolled " into sheet form, and " drawn " to form tubes or wire; it can be " soldered ", " brazed ", or welded.

When cast, its ultimate tensile strength is between 10,160 Kg. and 11,176 Kg. per 25·4 mm.^{2} (10 and 11 tons per square inch), but after being " worked " (*i.e.* rolled or drawn) its tensile strength is increased up to between 14,224 Kg. and 20,320 Kg. (14 and 20 tons).

Copper is an excellent conductor of heat and electricity, ranking second only to silver in the latter respect, and is therefore used extensively in wire form for electric transmission lines, cables, wiring systems, and various other electric fittings. It is also used in the form of piping for hot or cold domestic water installations.

When used for pipes on engines or machines, especially those subjected to vibration (such as petrol and oil-feed pipes of aeroplanes, motor-cars, etc.), it is liable to " harden " with age, and consequently becomes somewhat brittle. This brittleness can be remedied by periodically " annealing " the pipes (*i.e.* heating to a red heat, then quenching in cold water). Because of its excellent heat-transfer qualities over long periods, copper is used also for the manufacture of soldering-iron " nose-pieces ".

It is also often mixed with other non-ferrous metals to form various alloys, such as brass, bronze, " cupro-nickel ", monel (trade term), etc.

Lead is obtained by mining lead ore and refining it. It is one of the heaviest metals, having a specific gravity of 11·4, is of a dull grey colour, of a soft nature, and is very malleable.

Lead is used for alloying with other metals, but is used alone for making pipes for plumbing work. It also forms the basis of " solder " used for tinsmith's work.

Electric-storage battery plates are formed of hardened lead, as are the " terminals ". It resists sulphuric acid and does not corrode in the atmosphere; for the latter reason, it is used in building work in the form of " flashing " (sheeting) for roof-joints, etc.

Lead can be easily " cast " or " rolled " into sheets, and " drawn " to form pipes or wire.

It is also the basis of " zinc ", which is used extensively as a protective coating for iron and steel, in order to resist corrosion, such as in the form of galvanised corrugated steel sheeting.

Tin is also obtained by mining and smelting the ore, and is often found in conjunction with lead.

When refined, it is of a bright silvery colour, malleable, does not tarnish easily, and resists corrosion well. It is rarely used alone, except for " tinning " (coating iron and steel), etc., but is used extensively with other metals to form various alloys, *e.g.* bronze is a copper–tin alloy.

Nickel. This is still another metal obtained from ore deposits. It is a white silvery colour in its commercial refined state, and a hard, malleable metal, which resists corrosion, but tarnishes in due course. It is used as a " deposit " for " electro-plating " work, but is now more extensively used in conjunction with chromium for " plating " work, and is employed considerably in alloy form, such as nickel steel, monel metal, inconel, and stainless steels.

Aluminium. This metal is obtained from the mineral " bauxite ". After smelting and refining, it is a silvery-grey colour; very light, having a specific gravity of 2·7, and is soft and malleable. It can be " cast " or " rolled " to form sheets. When suitably alloyed, it has lightness combined with strength, and is used extensively for aircraft work and in the motor-car industry. In rolled sheet form its ultimate tensile strength is approximately 18,288 Kg. per 25·4 mm.^{2} (18 tons per square inch). Castings formed of the metal are often somewhat brittle. It resists corrosion well, and can nowadays be soldered and welded by a special process. One of the most common alloys is " duralumin ", from which, in addition to sheets being formed, it can also be " forged " or used for " stampings ", and cast to form engine-pistons and crankcases, etc.

Owing to its lightness and relatively good electrical conductivity, aluminium is now used for overhead electric supply lines. It is also used for making tubes or pipes, and for domestic cooking utensils.

" Alclad " is yet another form of " duralumin " sheet, but is coated on both sides with almost pure aluminium, thereby combining strength with special corrosion-resisting properties.

This material is therefore used to a large extent for chemical plant machinery of certain types.

Having introduced briefly to the reader some of the most common NON-FERROUS metals, consideration may now be given to certain alloys formed from them.

NON-FERROUS ALLOYS

Brass. This is possibly one of the largest used alloys in mechanical engineering, and undoubtedly one of the oldest employed.

It is of a bright yellow (or golden) colour, although its colour varies slightly according to its composition or " mix ".

It is composed of copper and zinc, of which the proportion may vary from 55 to 80 per cent. (or more) of copper, depending on its intended use.

Brass may be " cast ", " rolled " into sheets, or " drawn " to form tubes, wire and rods, etc.

A fair average " mix " for " casting " quality may be taken as 60 per cent. copper and 40 per cent. zinc, with slight variations for specific purposes.

The proportions of 70 per cent. and 30 per cent. zinc are more usual for brass suitable for " rolling " or " drawing ". This gives a somewhat softer quality, but increases its tenacity to the region of approximately 20,320 Kg. per $25 \cdot 4$ mm.^{2} (20 tons per square inch).

Brass is a good conductor of heat and electricity, is hard and durable, may be forged, can be easily "soft-soldered" or "brazed" (hard-soldered), and can now, by taking special precautions, be welded. It does not corrode, yet "tarnishes" easily, and if a very small amount of tin is added to the " mix " it resists the action of sea-water very well.

It can be polished to a very high degree, and on that account is used considerably for domestic appliances, architectural fittings, etc., in addition to normal " castings ", brackets, bolts, pipes, etc., for general engineering work.

It is also used extensively for electrical fittings, chiefly because of its resistance to corrosion and having good electrical conductivity.

Gun-metal. This material closely resembles brass, except that its colour may be slightly darker, owing to its higher copper content.

An average " mix " contains approximately 90 per cent. copper and 10 per cent. tin.

What is normally termed " Admiralty " gun-metal also usually contains about 2 per cent. zinc, and the copper content is about 88 per cent.; the remaining 10 per cent. being tin.

It is a hard, tough, close-grained alloy, and wears very well. It makes fine castings; is used extensively for "linings" of bearings (often called "brasses"), and is frequently employed for high-class architectural fittings, valves, steam-engine fittings, etc.

Gun-metal is sometimes called "bronze", and some types of "brass" are frequently referred to by this term, especially if in the form of a statue or figure. Church bells are mostly made of gun-metal, owing to its durability, combined with its close texture resulting in a fine product for the "casting" and its clear resonance, or sound-imparting qualities.

Aluminium-bronze is a mixture of aluminium, copper, and manganese, in varying proportions, but only up to about 10 per cent. of the last is added.

The product makes fine castings, giving a tenacity up to about 32,482 Kg. per 25·4 mm.^{2} (32 tons per square inch).

It is hard wearing, resists corrosion, and resists certain acids. On account of this last property, it is used for dairy machinery of some types in order to resist the "lactic" acid in milk. Its colour closely resembles that of brass and is sometimes used as a cheap substitute for 9 ct. gold, *e.g.* in fountain pen clips.

Phosphor-bronze is a copper–tin alloy with the addition of about 0·25 per cent. of phosphorus.

It is chiefly used for castings, as the addition of the phosphorus increases the materials' tenacity and renders it more durable. It is used for high-class gear-teeth, coil-type springs, or may be formed into wire for special purposes, and is extensively used for bearings of heavy industrial machinery, boiler fittings, etc.

The material is also unaffected by sea water, thereby lending itself well for marine work, especially propeller manufacture.

Manganese-bronze. By the addition of a certain quantity of manganese and a small percentage of iron and tin to gun-metal or bronze, the resulting products' tenacity is increased still further.

Its uses are rather similar to those of phosphor-bronze. In addition to forming castings, it can also be rolled or forged, and is used for making hydraulic machinery.

Monel Metal (Trade Term). This alloy is composed chiefly of nickel (about 70 per cent.), copper (about 29 per cent.) and iron (about 1 per cent.). It is very strong, having a tenacity of over 40,640 Kg. per 25·4 mm.² (40 tons per square inch), and is of close grain formation.

It can be " cast ", " rolled ", or " drawn ", and is widely used for valve seatings of aero-engines, valves and fittings for chemical machinery, ship propeller-shafts, etc.

The alloy is of a white-silvery colour, polishes up beautifully, does not tarnish, and possesses good heat- and acid-resisting qualities.

In many respects it is similar to stainless steel, particularly in colour, and to a large extent is used for similar purposes.

Inconel (Trade Term) is an alloy of approximately 76 per cent. nickel, 15 per cent. chromium, and the remaining 9 per cent. is chiefly iron. It is strong, malleable, and can be " cast " or drawn into wire or tubes, resists heat and corrosion admirably, but is not quite so resistive to sea-water as monel metal.

In the form of hard-drawn wire an ultimate tensile stress of 80 tons per square inch is obtainable, and it is used for multiple purposes, among which are machines for chemical plants, dairy work, oil burner-jets, etc.

For further detailed information the reader is referred to any book on " Metallurgy ", or " Strength and Testing of Materials ".

PLASTICS

In addition to metals and their alloys used in engineering, of recent years various " plastics " have been rapidly developed, and are now used extensively, especially for light classes of work.

Formerly vulcanite and compositions of rubber were used, chiefly in connection with electrical apparatus (on account of their excellent insulating properties). The same materials were used also for handles, knobs, etc., of machines, but recently various " plastics " have also been widely used for similar purposes.

In addition, owing to their being easily moulded into various shapes, plastics are used extensively for forming light brackets, gear-wheels, etc., for machinery.

Plastics comprise several forms, most of which are of the cellulose acetate (or nitrate), polyethylene, vinyl resin, or nylon bases.

Colouring matter can easily be incorporated with these plastics, which gives them an attractive appearance. They can be made very hard (in pressed, or moulded form). Some can also be made of a flexible nature and used in the form of tubes and pipes.

The moulded forms are, however, liable to be somewhat brittle.

" Perspex " (trade term) is another form of plastic material, and is transparent, whereby it can be used in place of glass for the inspection panels of some machines.

Plastics are now widely used in the aeroplane and automobile industries for forming panels, handles and casings for instruments, etc., in addition to many similar uses for general mechanical engineering instruments, also for domestic utensils, etc.

Occasionally during the machining process of an expensive casting " flaws " or small " blow-holes ", etc., may be detected, which up to that stage might have escaped detection. Such faults may render a casting " porous ", but in order to avoid " scrapping " it, the casting may be immersed in an enclosed vessel and hot liquid plastic material forced under pressure or injected into it, thus filling all the pores and making it serviceable for some classes of work.

The process is suitable for components such as small intricate cast brackets, housings, etc., but is unsuitable for valves, and hydraulic machinery subjected to high internal pressures, or those working under high temperatures.

APPENDIX A

A new form of cast iron has been devised during the last few years, known as " Spheroidal Graphite " iron. This has been achieved by altering the graphite grain structure formation from " flake " form to " rosette " or " spherical " form. By so doing, this produces a much stronger and more ductile product. The tensile strength has also been increased considerably and the material will deform before breaking. Its toughness has been doubled and its strength increased by from four to twelve times, as compared with ordinary " grey " cast iron, and its brittleness has been considerably reduced.

Many types of intricate components, which were formerly made by expensive forging methods, such as engine crankshafts and camshafts, are now made in the form of castings in " Spheroidal " iron.

This material is now being used widely for motor-car engine connecting rods, and at a much cheaper rate than by forging methods.

APPENDIX B

International agreement has recently been reached in regard to outside diameters, thicknesses and pipe threads and these agreements are set out in the I.S.O. (International Standards Organisation) recommendations shown on the following list:—

I.S.O. 87	Pipe Threads for Gas List Tubes and Screwed Fittings.
I.S.O. R.64	Steel Tubes—outside diameters.
I.S.O. R.50	Steel Sockets.
I.S.O. R.65	Steel Tubes suitable for screwing in accordance with I.S.O. Recommendation R.7.
I.S.O. R.221	Steel Tubes—thickness.
I.S.O. R.336	Plain and Steel Tubes welded or seamless, general table of dimensions and masses per unit length.
I.S.O. R.559	Steel Pipes for gas, water and sewage, welded or seamless.
I.S.O. R.560	Cold drawn precision steel tubes—Metric series, dimensions, tolerances and masses per metre.

The outside diameters and thicknesses agreed for steel tubes are based on the concept of " corresponding sizes ", i.e. for each size there is both a metric and an inch dimension, which whilst they may not be exact conversions, do in all cases ensure practicable interchangeability.

In general, therefore, the change to the metric system will not involve any change in the physical size of pipes and fittings as supplied at present, as the relevant British Standards are revised by the metric system, they will require the pipes to be ordered by the metric diameters and thicknesses instead of inch based values. This situation applied to screwed tubes and tubulars to B.S. 1387 and to pipes and tubes to B.S. 3601/5, B.S. 1775 and related application standards. Other related British Standards, such as B.S. 1740—Wrought Pipe Fittings, Iron and Steel, Screwed B.S.P. Threads, and B.S. 10—Flanges and Bolting for Pipe Valves and Fittings, and B.S. 21—Pipe Threads, are at present being considered by British Standards Institution from the aspect of Metrication.

The only case where any change in the physical size of pipes and tubes will be experienced in changing to the metric system is that of precision cold drawn steel tubes for which the sizes in I.S.O. R.560 will be adopted.

The student, however, is strongly advised to keep a look-out for any new or amended British Standards which may be issued by The British Standards Institution during the next few years appertaining to Pipes, Tubes and Fittings.

CHAPTER XII

TESTING OF MATERIALS

TESTS carried out on materials may be divided into two classes : " destructive " and " non-destructive ".

In the former case the " specimen " during its test is destroyed, and consequently is of no further use, beyond having served its purpose of indicating certain characteristics as to the " batch " or " mix " of metal from which it was made.

With regard to " non-destructive " tests, these can be performed on any " finished " article, prior to its intended use—for during such a test the article (or specimen) is not destroyed.

In this category is the " permeability " test, which is applicable only to materials susceptible to magnetism. It involves " magnetising " the metal, then de-" magnetising " it (i.e. inducing the property of " residual magnetism " into the specimen, until it reaches saturation ; then de-magnetising it). The amount of current required for the process is very carefully measured, and recorded on delicate electrical apparatus. This gives some indication of the quality of the specimen, for as a rule soft iron or steel is easily magnetised up to saturation point, whereas harder qualities require more current, or take a longer period to become fully magnetised.

In the same category comes another test, the " X-ray ", which, to describe briefly, is taking an X-ray photograph of the specimen. This test serves a useful purpose for detecting internal " flaws ", blow-holes, or cracks, in castings and welded work.

Normally a cracked casting can readily be detected if gently struck by a hammer and noting the " *dull* " tone of the sound emitted, as compared with the clear tone given by a perfect casting.

Other non-destructive tests are also used, but are beyond the scope of the introduction given in this book.

Tensile Test. Of the " destructive " or " damageable " tests, two of the most commonly used are : the " tensile ", and " hardness " types. The former consists of exerting a "tensile" (pulling) force on the specimen and carefully recording its characteristics until it breaks. The final, or breaking load is known as its "ultimate" stress, and is denoted in "tons per square inch" of the material. This test is undoubtedly the most extensively used of all types, and is therefore one with which all students of engineering should, at an early stage, become acquainted.

The stages through which the specimen passes during such a test are briefly outlined as follows:—

It is first prepared by machining the metal to specific dimensions and shape, as shown in Fig. 181. The ends are

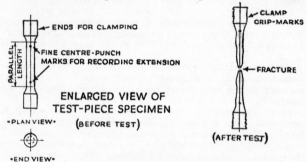

Fig. 181.

made of suitable size to fit into the "jaws" of the machine-clamps, but the centre portion is reduced (for a parallel length), to a convenient diameter. Usually this is either 25·4 mm. (1 inch) (*i.e.* giving a cross-sectional area of 501·450 mm.² (0·785 square inch), or the dimension to give a final cross-sectional area of 645·16 mm.² (exactly 1 square inch). The length is either 203·200 mm. or 254·000 mm. (8 or 10 inches), respectively, the latter being a very convenient one. Two fine marks are made at a specific distance apart in order for the "stretch" to be measured.

The testing machine consists essentially of a stout beam resembling a huge "Roman balance"—or "steelyard"—mounted on a strong frame, and on a knife-edge "hardened" steel fulcrum or pivot. On the beam is mounted an adjustable sliding balance weight. At the positions indicated in Fig. 181*a* suitable "clamps" are attached; the top one, to the beam and the lower clamp, is secured to some type of tensioning device, which is usually in the form of a hydraulic ram-plunger, or a stout screw operated electrically. Fig. 181*a* illustrates the hydraulic ram type.)   Some machines have a graduated scale along which slides the indicator-pointer of the balance weight, and the movement of this weight is operated via gearing by the hand-wheel mounted on the main frame-work.

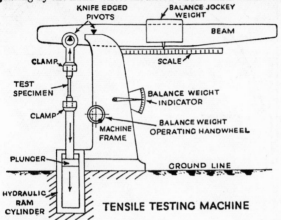

TENSILE TESTING MACHINE

Fig. 181a.

After the specimen has been securely clamped in the machine, the hydraulic ram is set in motion.   As this travels on its downward stroke, a " tensile " force is exerted on the "test specimen".   At the same time, the operator causes the weight on the beam to travel along it, whereby equalising or balancing the "tension" exerted by the ram.   As the ram-pressure increases, the specimen is "stretched" or extended.

Some machines have attached to them automatic devices which draw a " stress–strain " graph, thus recording the loads and extensions continually throughout the procedure. Alternatively, a record can be kept of the extension at each subsequent ton load, and a graph plotted afterwards (a typical example of this is shown in Fig. 182).   The extension is in that case measured by attaching to the test-piece an instrument called an " extensometer " (which is detached prior to the anticipated " breaking " load).

At the start of the test, when the initial load is applied, the stretch or extension is scarcely noticeable, but as the load is gradually increased this stretch becomes more apparent.

If, after a comparatively small load has been applied, it is released, the " stretch " so far realised in the specimen will

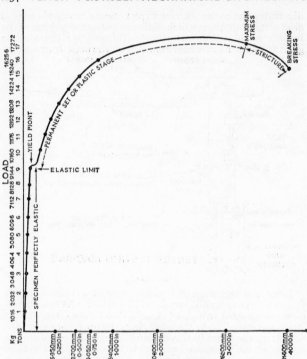

Fig. 182.—" Stress-strain " or Load-extension Graph (for
Wrought Iron Test-piece 10 Inches Long, 1 Inch Diameter
or 0·785 Square Inch Area).

disappear, and the length will revert to its original one. This
is known as the " elastic " stage. Such elasticity is very
noticeable in ductile materials, such as wrought iron, mild
steel, etc., but is less apparent in other metals or alloys of a
" harder " and more " brittle " nature.

If, instead of releasing the load, as just described, it is
increased continually, a stage will be reached at which the
specimen passes its " elastic " one. This is known as the
"elastic limit" or "yield point", beyond which the material
develops what is termed " permanent set " or " plasticity ".

As the load increases, so is the specimen stretched, until it reaches its breaking point (called the " ultimate stress "). Before doing so, however, it passes what is termed the " maximum load "—which is used for commercial purposes, as the " ultimate stress ". This apparent difference is accounted for because, after passing the maximum load (or stress), the material does not stretch evenly or at a uniform rate, but begins to " strickle " or extend irregularly, and in so doing (owing to its cross-sectional area being correspondingly reduced considerably below its original one) the specimen finally breaks at some place where the area is less, and at some load smaller than the maximum one just previously passed.

These foregoing " terms " will no doubt be better understood on reference being made to the typical "stress-strain" graph shown in Fig. 182, which is intended to acquaint the reader with the various stages passed through during the test. It will be noticed, however, that in this case, the diameter of the specimen being 25·4 mm (1 inch), its resulting cross-sectional area is 0·785 inch, from which can easily be calculated the relative loads for 25·4 mm.^{2} (1 square inch) area of the metal.

HARDNESS TESTS

" Brinell " Type. This test consists of pressing into the surface of the specimen a very hard steel ball—usually of 10 mms. diameter. The pressure is applied evenly, and the extent of indentation resulting in the specimen is carefully measured across its diameter and depth.

Certain values (or numerals) have been adopted and tabulated for the relative degrees of hardness of various materials, from which comparisons can be made with specimens tested.

Vickers System. In general principle this somewhat resembles the "Brinell" test, except that, instead of using a hard steel ball to effect the penetration, an inverted, pyramid-shaped diamond is employed. By this means it is claimed the diamond better resists the partial distortion which may be experienced with the steel ball, especially when used for testing metals of a comparatively hard nature. In this case a different table of values is used, known as V.P.N. numbers, instead of the " Brinell " tables.

Other tests for a metal's hardness are also made, but those just described will, it is hoped, suffice to acquaint the reader with the basic principles involved.

A full table of ISO Metric Screw Threads is given on pages 183–5 of Mechanical Engineering Volume I, *Hand Tools.*

METRIC TABLES

Note : The *metre* is the unit

1 decimetre	$\frac{1}{10}$	of the unit	
1 centimetre	$\frac{1}{100}$	,,	,,
1 millimetre	$\frac{1}{1000}$	,,	,,
1 metre	is the unit		
1 dekametre	10	times the unit	
1 hectometre	100	,,	,,
1 kilometre	1000	,,	,,
1 myriametre	10,000	,,	,,

METRIC LINEAR TABLE

10 millimetres (mm.)	1 centimetre (cm.)
10 centimetres	1 decimetre (dm.)
10 decimetres	1 metre (m.)
10 metres	1 dekametre
10 dekametres	1 hectometre
10 hectometres	1 kilometre (Km.)
10 kilometres	1 myriametre

METRIC SQUARE MEASURE

100 square millimetres	1 square centimetre (cm.^{2})
100 ,, centimetres	1 ,, decimetre (dm.^{2})
100 ,, decimetres	1 ,, metre (m.^{2})
100 ,, metres	1 ,, dekametre
100 ,, dekametres	1 ,, hectometre
100 ,, hectometres	1 ,, kilometre (Km.^{2})

METRIC WEIGHT

10 milligrams	1 centigram (cg.)
10 centigrams	1 decigram (dg.)
10 decigrams	1 gram (gm.)
10 grams	1 dekagram (Dg.)
10 dekagrams	1 hectogram (Hg.)
10 hectograms	1 kilogram (Kg.)
1000 kilograms	1 *metric* ton

INDEX

237